'With Trevor in no fit state to drive, it was nice of you to offer me a lift. But I can do without your comments on my relationship with my boyfriend,' said Genieve.

'I planned to drive you home from the moment I saw you,' Ross said calmly, correcting her assumption.

Her heart seemed to skip a beat. She'd wanted to ignore the magnetism of attraction between them. She still wanted to, despite Ross's statement.

'Why?' she demanded, intending to warn him off with hostility while her skin prickled with awareness.

The traffic lights changed to amber and then green and, as the Jaguar surged forward, he said, 'You know why.' His voice was even, yet there was something intent and telling in it, making her feel almost breathless for an instant. The response of her senses told her that Ross was right. She did know. But she also knew she was terrified of being hurt again.

FRAGILE PARADISE

BY

JENNY ARDEN

MILLS & BOON LIMITED
ETON HOUSE   18–24 PARADISE ROAD
RICHMOND   SURREY   TW9 1SR

*First published in Great Britain 1990
by Mills & Boon Limited*

© Jenny Arden 1990

*Australian copyright 1990
Philippine copyright 1990
This edition 1990*

ISBN 0 263 76890 2

*Set in 10 on 12 pt Linotron Times
01-9012-48014
Typeset in Great Britain by Centracet, Cambridge
Made and printed in Great Britain*

CHAPTER ONE

GENIEVE folded the letter she had been re-reading and thrust it into her dressing-table drawer. She bit her lip, her eyes troubled. Just to hear again from the man who had caused her so much heartbreak over the past two years would have upset her, but the news his letter had contained had thrown her into a panic all day.

It made her wish she was staying quietly at home this evening. She had never felt less like going out to a party. There was an angry ache beneath her ribs, an ache she had only recently begun to forget. Impulsively she jerked the dressing-table drawer open, took the letter out and ripped it in two. The small violent action did her good, making her feel stronger.

She stood up and glanced at the clock radio by her bed. Even if she'd wanted to, it was too late now to phone Trevor to cancel their date. He would already be on his way to pick her up.

Breathing in deeply, she resolved not to let the unexpected communication she had received that morning ruin her evening. She was not only going to her cousin's party. She was going to master her emotions and enjoy herself tonight.

Debating what to wear, she paced over to her wardrobe in her lace-trimmed camisole and briefs. Her hand travelled along the rail, hesitated at a mischievous fringed red shift, then moved on to a short draped and frilled number in black and gold. The pain around her heart was still there, albeit masked by a mutinous defiance, and the seductive gypsy dress matched her mood. She drew it out. Holding it in front of her, she looked at her reflection in the mirror. A slender red-head gazed back at her. She was tall and graceful with high cheekbones, rather severe eyebrows and an ivory complexion. Her smoky-blue eyes were thickly fringed with auburn-tipped lashes, her nose was straight, her mouth generous. A fall of glossy Titian hair set off her features.

In her mid-twenties, she had a poise that distinguished her immediately in a room full of people. Her smoky-blue eyes were cool, yet provocative. She had built up her defences well since her broken love affair. No one would have guessed that beneath the self-assured façade was a vulnerable woman who had been hurt once, and hurt badly.

The doorbell rang as she was applying her mascara. She finished sweeping the brush over her long lashes. Then, picking up her earrings, she ran downstairs with lithe grace to open the door to Trevor.

Broad-shouldered and blond, he looked rich, indolent and charming in his dark dinner jacket. He worked for an investment house in the City, and Genieve had met him some six weeks ago at the country club where she went occasionally to play squash or to enjoy a swim.

She hadn't felt she was ready to make another relationship, but Trevor had been persistent and finally she had agreed to go out for a drink with him. One date had led to another, and lately they had been seeing a lot of each other.

'Hello, Trevor,' she began, kissing him lightly on the cheek. 'Come on in. I'm afraid I'm not quite ready.'

'What's new?' he teased.

Her lips curved in a rueful smile. 'Punctuality was never one of my strong points.'

The front door opened straight into the lounge and she stood back to let him in. It was an attractive room with its white walls, dark beams and windows that looked on to the street.

She lived on her own, and the small but characterful cottage on the upper slopes of Harrow Hill suited her well. When she had bought it, the cottage had been in need of renovating but, quick to see its potential, Genieve had fallen in love with it straight away. Although the alterations had been a lot of work, she had enjoyed seeing the place take shape, and the impression it now gave was one of brightness, ease and comfort.

'Would you like a drink while you're waiting?' she asked, fastening her earrings as she spoke.

'No, thanks.' Trevor sat down on the sofa and reached for the newspaper that was on the coffee-table. 'I'll see what I can do with the crossword instead.'

'OK. I won't be long.'

She put the final touches to her make-up, twisted her hair into a chic chignon and sprayed her pulse points lightly with the perfume that was her signature, Rive Gauche. Her silk shawl was lying on the bed, and she picked it up and draped it over her arm. After a rather disappointing summer the first week of September had been beautiful, with temperatures well in the seventies, meaning that she didn't need a jacket.

Trevor glanced up, hearing her light step on the stairs.

'You're certainly worth waiting for,' he approved. 'You look gorgeous.'

'Thank you. Have you finished the crossword?'

'All but one clue,' he said. 'What's an American pony called?'

Genieve thought for an instant, then suggested, 'A mustang?'

'Too long. It's got to be six letters.'

'How about bronco, then?' she said, looking over his shoulder at the newspaper.

'I think you've solved it.' He filled in the answer and announced with satisfaction, 'There, finished. Come on, let's go.'

Genieve's cousin, who ran an art gallery, lived in Chelsea. Trevor hadn't met her before and was interested in knowing a little more about her. Obligingly Genieve told him that Coralie was a talented and ambitious career woman.

'Is she married?' he asked.

'Yes, but she and her husband are separated. I expect they'll divorce in the end, but it's a pity. I always liked Geoff and I think he was good for Coralie.'

'In what way?' asked Trevor.

He was driving with the sun-roof of his Lotus open, and she brushed a wisp of windblown hair from her face as she answered, 'Coralie's the restless type. She's full of enthusiasm for something one minute and the next it's played out and she's got another scheme in mind. Geoff was far more pragmatic. In many ways they were complete opposites, but they seemed to complement each other.'

'So you think opposites attract,' Trevor quipped.

Genieve's expressive eyes darkened a little. She knew

just how strong that attraction could be, just as she knew that beneath it there had to be a similarity of outlook if it was ever to form the basis of a stable, lasting relationship. Pushing the memories aside, she said, wishing Trevor hadn't reminded her of the past, 'They can do.'

'And how alike do you think we are?' he asked, flirting with her.

'We haven't been going out together long. I need time to make a judgement like that.'

Trevor chuckled. But despite her teasing answer, her heart wasn't in the banter. Neither was it in the conversation she kept up with him for the next twenty minutes, though he wasn't perceptive enough to notice it.

The Lotus had just turned off the busy Western Avenue when he remarked, 'You've gone very quiet suddenly.'

'Hmm?' she said absently, her gaze swinging to him.

'I said you've gone very quiet,' he repeated.

'I. . . I was thinking,' she said with the ghost of an apologetic laugh.

'What about?'

'Oh, just this and that.'

She and Trevor weren't close enough for her to tell him that she felt upset because the man she'd once loved deeply had written to her, though in any case, always a shade reserved, she believed that hurt was best buried deep. She wanted to forget Paul and everything he had meant to her, not talk about him.

'Ever the woman of mystery,' Trevor quipped. 'Anyway, now that I've got your attention again, why don't we arrange what we're going to do tomorrow?

After the party we'll be too tired to think of anything original.'

Hoping that if she feigned gaiety long enough it might become genuine, Genieve teased, 'Did you have something original in mind?'

'Not really,' he joked. 'But I'll work on it.'

When they arrived at her cousin's penthouse apartment the party was in full swing. Coralie's spacious split-level cream and beige lounge was thronged with people. The buzz of conversation mingled with bursts of laughter and the throb of music.

Her cousin threaded her way across the crowded room to greet them. In her early thirties, Coralie would have passed for no more than twenty-seven. As beautifully made as a racehorse, she was tall and redheaded like Genieve, though totally different in looks. Yet even so people often mistook them for sisters.

She was wearing a black lace top with emerald satin harem pants which matched her eyes and set off her figure to perfection.

'I'm so glad you could come,' she began, brushing her cheek against Genieve's in a quick social kiss. 'I haven't seen you for ages.'

'That's because you're always off on some business trip or another,' Genieve laughed.

'True—and what's more, I've got another one lined up soon.' Coralie turned to Trevor, giving him a dazzling smile as she asked Genieve, 'And who's this? A friend of yours?'

Genieve introduced the two of them, mildly amused by the glint of masculine appreciation in Trevor's eyes as he said hello to her cousin. Coralie's siren-like charm seemed to stop all men in their tracks, and Trevor was no exception.

The three of them chatted for a while, then Genieve's cousin said to her, 'I think you know most of the people here, so I'll leave you to circulate. There's someone I want you to meet later on, but he hasn't arrived yet.' She touched Trevor lightly on the arm. 'You must tell me more about what you do as soon as I have a minute. It sounds fascinating.'

As she wandered off Trevor murmured, 'Your cousin's quite something.'

'Should I be jealous?' Genieve teased as she sipped her drink.

'You know I've only got eyes for you,' he protested. He slipped his arm round her waist while his gaze travelled over the room that was noisy with at least a dozen witty conversations. 'Coralie has some interesting friends. I take it they're mostly from the art world.'

She was doing her best to forget the aching of a wound she had deluded herself had healed. It would have helped had the party not reminded her so vividly of the last party she had been to with Paul.

'They think they're gifted,' she said. 'Some of them are but mostly they're dilettantes, while half the art collectors here tonight would rave over a road sign if it had the name Picasso scrawled along the bottom. All they're interested in is art as an investment.'

'So?' said Trevor.

'So I think that's wrong. Pictures should belong to people who care about them.'

'I didn't know you felt so passionately about art?' he said, giving her a quizzical look.

She hunched her shoulders in a slight shrug. Instead

of answering him, she said, 'Why don't we dance? I like Bob Marley.'

'I'd rather mingle a bit first.' His drink in his hand, he pointed to a slim blonde in a strapless tube dress edged with net. 'Isn't that Lord Winchcombe's daughter with fiancé number three?'

'So what?' Genieve said, not ready to judge when her own romance had been ill-fated. 'Perhaps she's been unlucky in love.'

'Is that spoken from the heart?' Trevor frowned.

'Maybe, maybe not,' she quipped, trying to lighten things between them.

Deep down she was miserable and worried about what she was going to do when Paul came back to England. On top of it she couldn't cope with Trevor in a sullen mood. Their relationship had been nicely low-key at first, but lately, with his pestering her to sleep with him, and his annoyance when she said no, friction was creeping into their friendship.

The friction was there again now as Trevor growled in an angry undertone, 'Are you going to expand on that answer?'

She took a handful of nuts from a nearby bowl. At her most beguiling and flippant, she said simply, 'No.'

Scowling, he took a sip of whisky before demanding, 'What makes you so damned elusive and complicated?'

'I warned you at the start not to get serious about me, and you said that was fine,' she replied. 'We've had some good times together, and I'd like to have a good time tonight. So let's call a halt to this conversation or we'll end up rowing.'

'You're the one who's trying to pick a row,' he said.

'When you put your mind to it you can be bloody difficult.'

'I take it you're referring to my strange unwillingness to leap into bed with you,' she answered, coldly sarcastic because she knew full well that was what had prompted his comment. 'Have you labelled me as easy, or is it that you think your charm is irresistible?'

'For God's sake!' he exploded with muted force. 'Yes, I'd like us to be sleeping together. I don't go in for platonic relationships. It's more than time you told me where the hell I stand with you.'

'Don't get possessive, Trevor. It's boring.'

'I have a perfect right to be possessive,' he ground back, taking hold of her by the arm. 'I've been dating you for six weeks.'

'A lifetime! Now back off, will you? You don't own me; nobody does.'

With that she snatched her arm free. As she did so her gaze collided with a pair of dark eyes that stopped hers with a blaze of insolent interest. She had no idea who the man was, but it was apparent that he had only just arrived. She sensed rather than saw the way heads turned to where he stood in the doorway as the focus of the party shifted in his direction.

His gaze continuing to hold hers, he raised one dark brow in mock salute. He had obviously witnessed, if not the whole of her exchange with Trevor, certainly the last part of it. Her blue eyes sparked with anger and hostility, and a smile twitched the corners of his firm mouth in response. She pulled her gaze away without smiling back as he was promptly drawn into a laughing group.

An acquaintance of hers was standing near the

stereo. Andrew Chandler was a financier and hedonist
who thrived on a highly pressurised lifestyle. Genieve
joined him, deliberately turning her back on the man
who had been watching her.

'Genieve!' Andrew exclaimed delightedly. He caught
hold of both her hands as he kissed her. 'How are you?'

'Hello, Andrew,' she laughed. 'Long time, no see.'

'Too long. Let me look at you.'

She pirouetted round, her flounced skirt twirling to
show off long, chorus-line legs in sheer black stockings.

'My God, you're more beautiful than ever,' Andrew
murmured. 'Who's the lucky dog who's with you
tonight?'

'Trevor? He's just a friend,' she answered, accepting
the cigarette Andrew offered her.

He snapped open his engraved gold lighter. She
leaned towards the flame, inhaled deeply and then with
a slight lift of her chin blew smoke over his shoulder.
She was glad of the cigarette to calm her nerves and her
temper.

In spite of herself she turned slightly, her glance
guarded. But the man with the cynically amused brown
eyes was no longer watching her. Instead he was talking
to the people he was with. Alice Quinn, a friend of her
cousin's, was hanging on to his arm as well as his every
word.

Genieve looked away. It was crazy, but she felt in
need of a moment's grace to collect herself. Her clash
with Trevor had been private, not some diversion laid
on for a stranger's entertainment. Yet mingled with her
anger there was a strange, unwilling awareness that
their exchange of glances has been in some way
significant.

Realising that she'd missed what Andrew had asked her, she said, 'Sorry. What did you say?'

'I thought Paul would be here with you tonight.'

'You're out of touch, Andrew,' she said with a twisted smile. 'That was all over six months ago.'

'What happened?' he enquired.

Genieve hunched her shoulders.

'We split up. End of story.'

'So now you're footloose and fancy free.'

'More or less,' she agreed, flirting with him in return.

'And looking bewitchingly Bohemian.'

A cameo vase of old gold carnations and copper red roses graced the console table behind him.

'Didn't Carmen have a rose?' he went on, taking one of them out of the vase, snapping its long stem and handing it to her.

Coralie won't thank you for dismantling her flower arrangement,' she joked, tucking the rose in her bodice.

'You're quite right!' her cousin announced at her elbow. She gave Andrew a glare of mock annoyance and went on, 'I've been looking for you, Genieve. There's someone I want you to meet. Ross, this is my cousin.'

Unsuspectingly Genieve turned, her lips parting slightly and a faint tinge of colour coming into her face as she looked up into the dark eyes of the man who not so long ago had silently made fun of her. He was tanned and attractive, his urbane masculinity enhanced by his dark dinner jacket that moulded the lines of his powerful shoulders.

She judged him to be no more than thirty-four, yet maturity was stamped both in his physique and in his face. All his features were strong, from the hawkish

brows that were as black as his hair to the aggressive
thrust of his jaw. Though Coralie had brought him over
to meet her, there was no doubt that he was the sort of
man no woman, nor anyone else for that matter, would
ever lead around.

'Genieve,' her cousin completed the introduction,
'this is Ross Macauley, a very good friend of mine.'

'I wondered when I first saw you if you were related
to Coralie.' The remark was addressed solely to her.

His voice matched his looks. Deep and self-assured,
it held a touch of mocking humour, all that was needed
in her current mood to make her temper spark.

Tilting her chin to a defiant angle, she said coolly,
'Did you?'

'Have you two already met?' asked Coralie, puzzled
by their conversation.

'We collided, so to speak, earlier,' Ross replied.

Nettled by the taunting glint in his dark eyes,
Genieve said, 'Luckily it left no bruises. Will you excuse
me? There's someone I must say hello to.'

She felt his look of sardonic amusement between her
shoulder-blades as she crossed the crowded room.
Annoyed with herself for letting a total stranger make
her feel so antagonised and challenged, she glanced
around for Trevor.

Her gaze located him standing by the bar. He was
with a slender brunette who was giggling appreciatively
at one of his jokes. As he caught sight of Genieve he
deliberately put his arm around the girl's shoulders,
bending his head to nuzzle her neck. The brunette
giggled again.

Changing her mind about making up with him,

Genieve looked away and said in answer to the question she had just been asked, 'Yes, I'd love to dance.'

Later, a glass in one hand and the other free to straighten a tie or to offer a light caress, she said amusing things, teased and made small talk, while she wished she hadn't come. Despite the pretence, she wasn't enjoying the party one bit. If she and Trevor hadn't quarrelled she would have pleaded a headache and suggested that they leave early.

Andrew came up to her. Catching her about the waist, he began, 'I wondered where you'd got to.'

'Andrew, stop it!' she protested, then gave up struggling and allowed him to pull her closer. She had always liked him in a friendly sort of way. There was no harm in him or his teasing.

'When are you going to let me paint you?' he asked.

Going along with the banter, she said, 'You're a collector, Andrew, not an artist.'

'I've decided it's time that changed,' he quipped. 'You never know, I might have hidden talent.'

'What are you going to try? Landscapes?'

'No, nudes,' he returned in a wicked undertone.

She gave him a playful slap on the wrist, then caught her breath imperceptibly as her gaze was intercepted by Ross Macauley. He was standing chatting to her cousin and, as inadvertently her eyes clashed with his, she tried to put him down with a cold stare.

She realised her mistake as his dark brows drew together, hawkish interest coming into his brown eyes that held such a compelling hard brilliance. Despite the crush of people, the awareness between them was suddenly so potent that they might have been alone together. Far from freezing him with her stare, she

realised that unintentionally her look had been almost
a dare to his virility.

Thrown into confusion, she drained her Martini glass
and said to Andrew, 'I'm going to get another drink.'

She freed herself and crossed the space where couples
were dancing. She had almost reached the bar when
she all but collided with Ross as he deliberately stepped
into her path.

To her fury she found she was blushing. Trying to
conceal the fact that he had the ability to disturb as well
as antagonise her, she said coolly, 'Excuse me.'

But instead of standing aside he took her glass out of
her hand. Making a leisurely appraisal of her that made
her pulse flutter and her temper quicken, he asked,
'What are you drinking?'

'Nothing, thank you,' she said coldly.

An amused smile glinted in his eyes.

'Tell me, what's he done?' he asked as he set her
glass aside.

Unprepared for the question, she asked blankly,
'Who? Andrew?'

'No, the boyfriend.'

Putting yet more frost into her voice, she said, 'I
don't know what you mean.'

'First you pick a quarrel with him,' Ross answered
lazily, 'then you decide to ignore him. What's he done
to deserve it?'

Anger sparkled in her blue eyes. Had it been anyone
different she would have responded by turning on her
heel, but Ross wasn't a man to walk away from. Ruffled
and provoked by him, she cast a glance in Trevor's
direction. He was still with the slim brunette.

'He doesn't seem inconsolable,' she observed with sarcasm.

'What did you expect him to do? Sulk in a corner while you play fast and loose?'

Touched on the raw, she retorted, 'My behaviour is none of your business, Mr Macauley.'

'The name's Ross,' he reminded her. 'Now, shall we dance?'

His cheek was unbelievable.

'No, we won't,' she snapped.

'I suppose Trevor wouldn't like it,' he mocked.

'That's right!'

The grooves deepened on either side of his attractive mouth as he corrected her, 'If Trevor were the jealous sort he'd have exploded already, the way you've been skimming from man to man this evening.'

'You've got a damned nerve!'

'So I've been told,' he answered smoothly as, taking hold of her hand, he drew her into his arms.

'Let go of me!' she demanded furiously, her pulses clamouring with the shock of the physical contact with his hard man's body.

'Are you going to make a scene?' he jibed softly.

'Yes, if you don't let go of me!'

He looked down at her, a wealth of masculine knowledge in his shrewd dark eyes as he said,

'I don't think so. Your cousin now, she's another matter, but you, you're not the type.'

Her gaze clashed with his for an instant longer, before, seething inwardly, she conceded defeat.

'Do you enjoy manipulating people, Mr Macauley?' she asked, with all the more antagonism because it was

evident that she had more than met her match with
him.

'I've told you—the name's Ross.'

The live warmth of his hand moved lower on her slim
back. The fragrance of his aftershave was crisp and
subtle and as disturbingly male as the rest of him.
Aware that her heart was beating at an erratic pace,
Genieve quipped cuttingly, 'And you'd like me to use
it. Do you specialise in clichéd lines?'

His laugh was gravelly and attractive.

'I'm not surprised the boyfriend finds you too much
to handle. I should think your highly amusing reper-
toire's wasted on him.'

She bit back a reply. Ross noted the swift rise and
fall of her breasts that revealed her simmering anger,
then drew her closer into his embrace. She felt a blaze
of annoyance, but, since her sarcasm had no effect on
him, she decided she'd see what frosty silence could do.

Tactically it was a bad move. The music was slow and
romantic. More than that, there was something sensual
and alarmingly pleasant about being held against Ross's
body that was so much taller and more powerful than
her own slight form.

Her fingers were enclosed in the warm grip of his.
Quite plainly he was enjoying the feel of her in his
arms. As the music enfolded them, her defiance ebbed
a little and, without her meaning it to, her right hand
curled around his neck, smoothing his dark, well-cut
hair.

She wasn't sure how long she gave in to the wayward
enchantment before, with a slight jolt, she realised how
pliant she had become in his embrace. Her hostility
returning with a rush, she brought her hand down to

his shoulder, intent on establishing a safer distance between them.

As she did so her eyes met his, and electricity seemed to flicker along her nerves.

'Do you work at the gallery with Coralie?' he asked.

'No.'

His mouth quirked slightly at her unhelpful answer.

'Where do you work, then?' he persisted.

'In Northwood.'

The attractive smile that played around his mouth deepened.

'Having a conversation with you is hard work,' he remarked.

The track they had been dancing to ended and, taking advantage of the instant's pause before the next track began, Genieve disengaged herself from his embrace. It was much easier to be coolly defiant when she wasn't being held in his arms.

'How aggravating for you,' she jibed, intending the comment to be her parting shot.

But Ross was too quick for her. Taking hold of her by the arm, he drawled, 'Luckily I'm a patient man.' His grip wasn't firm, yet she sensed it would tighten the instant she tried to pull away. 'To date, all I know is that you're Coralie's cousin and that you've got a redhead's temper. Fill me in with a few more facts.'

Maddened that there was no getting the better of him, Genieve said, sweetly insolent, 'I'm twenty-five. I live in Harrow, run a boutique in Northwood, and my birth sign's Scorpio.'

A mocking dark eyebrow arched at her. The glint in his dark eyes invited her to share the joke with him. She fought against capitulating to his sense of humour, yet the temptation to answer the roguish charm of his mouth was too much.

In spite of herself she felt her throat quiver with suppressed laughter. Her hostility suddenly not only seemed childish, but was impossible to sustain. Her lips curved into an attractive smile, her first genuine smile of the evening.

'What birth sign are you?' she asked.

CHAPTER TWO

'TAURUS,' said Ross. 'I believe that's supposed to make us compatible, isn't it?'

'You're right,' Genieve replied, amused by his irony. 'It is.'

Someone had turned the music up, making it hard to talk.

'Rather than have to shout at each other, let's try the roof garden,' said Ross.

A number of other guests had also chosen to wander outside and stood chatting as couples, or in groups. Terracotta pots overflowing with flowers and greenery added to the chic urban charm of the setting, and as Genieve wandered over to the balustrade she caught the fragrance of alyssum and geraniums.

Leaning her arms along the solid wrought-iron rail, she gazed out over London. The night was warm and languid and the dark sky lofty and full of stars. The music filtered out faintly from the lounge. Even the noise of the traffic sounded remote.

Although it was late, the city still shone like a jewel-case of lights. She could see the street-lamps of Chelsea Embankment and those of Chelsea Bridge. Dancing silver shivers marked the placid expanse of the river which gleamed beyond the elegant buildings like an onyx mirror.

Despite having been brought up in rural Gloucestershire, she was very much a city person, and softly, musingly, almost to herself, she quoted, 'Oh, gleaming lights of London. . .'

'That gem the city's crown.' Ross's deep voice sounded at her elbow.

Startled, she turned to him, surprised that their thoughts should be so closely attuned. Her gaze took in the strong planes of his face and the exciting line of his jaw.

'You know the poem!' she remarked.

'Surprised?'

'A little,' she admitted, for he struck her as being dynamic and sardonic, a man with few illusions despite his sense of humour. With a smile that was teasing and attractive, she said, 'Somehow I can't quite see you reading poetry. It doesn't seem to fit your image.'

'Which proves you shouldn't make snap judgements about people,' he mocked.

Genieve turned from the balustrade. Finding that she was enjoying their conversation, which was sparky and unpredictable, she said, 'You don't believe in intuition, then?'

'My hunch that you were part of the art world was wrong,' he reminded her before asking, 'What's your boutique called?'

'Le Boudoir,' she said, adding to explain the name she had chosen, 'It's a lingerie shop.'

Most men couldn't resist making some quip. Ross's was more subtle than most.

'I suppose, as with women's sandals, the less there is of it, the more you pay?'

She laughed and said, 'Something like that.'

'How long have you been in business?'

'About three years,' she said, then observed, 'You ask a lot of questions.'

'OK. You ask me some for a change.'

The glint of a smile in his eyes acknowledged, without being blatant about it, that she was an attractive woman. It made her more than ever aware of the low-key electricity between them. It was just as well he was involved with her cousin, she thought. Had he been unattached she would have found him far too charismatic.

She shook her head and said, 'No, let me guess instead. First of all, with a name like Macauley, you're a Scot.'

'Very astute of you,' he said with humour.

'More than that,' she went on, 'I'd say you're a Scot who's never lived in Scotland. There's no trace of a Highland burr in your voice. Do I get full marks?'

'Half marks,' he stated. 'I lived in Edinburgh till I was ten, when my parents moved south.'

'Do you ever hanker to go back to Scotland?'

'At times. But I think I'll settle for buying a small cottage up there for weekends.'

They talked for a while longer, chiefly about property, until Alice came over to ask Ross his opinion of the David Hockney exhibition that was currently showing at the Tate. Deciding that perhaps it was time she made up with Trevor, Genieve moved away.

At the patio doors she glanced back. Alice, like her cousin, was attractive, self-assured and sophisticated. She was also in Genieve's experience a spiteful gossip.

Genieve watched as she smiled up into Ross's chiselled, swarthy face, then looked away again. She had enjoyed talking to him, but he meant nothing to her, and never would, so it was ridiculous to feel suddenly a shade lonely now they had parted.

She found Trevor at the bar.

'How nice to see you at last,' he began. His voice was tinged with sarcasm and slightly slurred. It was obvious he had spent most of the evening drinking, and she could tell from the aggressive scowl on his face that he was going to need careful handling to avoid another argument.

'The music was too loud in the lounge,' she explained.

'And you wanted some peace and quiet,' he sneered. 'Was that why you and that tall good-looking guy you were dancing with disappeared together?'

'Ross is Coralie's boyfriend.'

'Really?' he returned sarcastically.

'Yes, really,' she said. 'Now are you ready to make a move?'

'I'm regretting I ever bothered to come,' he said with a bitter laugh. 'You seem more than able to have a good time at a party minus my company.'

Thinking of the brunette he had spent much of the evening with, Genieve could have pointed out that the same was true of him. But, refusing to be drawn into an argument, she said, 'I'll just say goodnight to Coralie.'

Having done so she went into the guest bedroom which opened off the small but elegant hall. Trevor lounged in the doorway as she searched for her fringed shawl among the jackets and wraps that had been tossed on to the bed.

'I think you'd better let me have the car keys,' she said, as she turned back to him when she had found it.

'You mean these?' he taunted, jangling them in front of her.

'Yes,' she replied.

She made to take them, but as she did so he snatched them away from her.

'I'm not so drunk I need you to drive me home,' he said, as he pulled her close.

'Trevor, let go of me!' He was hurting her and she was beginning to lose patience with him.

'You enjoy playing the tease, don't you?' he sneered as she struggled, offended by the smell of whisky on his breath. Seeing her expression of distaste, he jeered, 'Fastidious as ever!'

'Let me go!'

'No, damn it, I won't,' he snarled, taking hold of her chin with savage fingers and bending his head.

His lips ground against hers and she gave a muffled cry of pain, striking her fist against his shoulder. Immediately he moved so that his body held her pinned against the wall, his mouth continuing to ravage hers. When, finally, he raised his head, she was sickened and shaking.

'You. . .you brute!' she said in a hoarse whisper.

'It's no more than you deserve,' he muttered, lust in his eyes.

'Stop it!' she gasped, fright beginning to mingle with her anger and revulsion. Desperately she tried to press back and away from him. But her efforts were futile. She held herself rigid and still, hearing her choked sound of distress as she waited for his mouth to find hers in another brutal kiss.

Instead, Trevor was pulled roughly away from her. Bewildered, and thankful to be free, Genieve looked up to see Ross. A wintry chill in his eyes, he addressed her boyfriend.

'I suggest you make yourself scarce,' he began grittily.

'You stay out of this!' snarled Trevor.

He made to give Ross an aggressive shove, but Ross was too quick for him. Sidestepping, he grabbed hold of him and jerked him against the wall.

'Scram,' he ordered contemptuously.

A nerve jumped in Trevor's cheek, but, lacking the courage to stand up to Ross, he sidled to the door. Pausing there, he said, 'I get it. You've taken a fancy to Genieve. Well, let me tell you something, you're wasting your time. Genieve here has a grudge against the whole of the male sex. Maybe some guy stood her up at some time, but whatever the cause, beneath the superficial warmth and charm, she's a frigid bitch. . .'

The insult was bitten off abruptly as Ross's palm cracked across his face.

'If you weren't drunk, you'd apologise for that,' he said in a dangerously quiet voice. He snatched Trevor's car keys from him. 'Now get out.'

As he staggered back to the lounge and the party Genieve turned away. Her knees were shaky and her throat felt tight. Trevor's scathing words cut all the more deeply for being so close to the truth.

She started as a pair of warm capable hands descended on her shoulders.

'Are you OK?' Ross asked gently.

Near to tears, she didn't trust her voice to answer. With far too much pride to want to cry in front of a man she hardly knew, she gave a little nod.

Ross turned her towards him. His gaze narrowed on

her, his brows coming together in a frown as he saw the red marks along her jaw left by Trevor's fingers.

'You're going to have bruises there tomorrow.'

She could feel his anger. Huskily she said, 'It. . .it doesn't matter. I bruise easily.'

'Splash some cold water on them,' he instructed. 'And then I'll drive you home.'

Blinking back tears, she nodded again. Once inside the en suite bathroom, with the door safely shut behind her, she buried her face in her hands. Her sobs stuck in her throat, hurting her as she fought them back. It took her several moments before she was sure she had them beaten. She turned the cold tap on over the washbasin and stared at herself in the mirror. Her eyes were still dangerously dark and bright. Badly shaken by the drunken anger with which Trevor had kissed her, she forced herself to stop replaying what he had said. If she thought of Paul now, she'd start crying for certain.

It was several minutes later when she returned to the bedroom. Ross was waiting for her in the hall.

'Ready?' he asked.

She looked up into his face with its strongly chiselled features. She was most grateful to him for rescuing her, but she didn't want to be a nuisance.

'It's very kind of you,' she said, 'but really, there's no need for you to drive me home. I can get a taxi.'

'Stubborn as well as independent,' Ross commented, teasing her gently, while at the same time making her realise that the subject was closed.

Her gaze went towards the lounge and, reading her thoughts he said, 'You don't have to worry about Trevor. I've given Coralie his car keys. She's agreed to call a cab for him.'

'Thanks. I don't want him driving when he's drunk.'

Ross's hawkish eyes narrowed on her for an instant. He made no remark. His car, a dark green Jaguar, was parked in a nearby side-street. As they walked towards it, Genieve said genuinely, 'I'm sorry I've dragged you away from the party. I hope Coralie didn't mind too much.'

'Why should she mind?' Ross asked, as though surprised by the question.

'I thought. . .' Genieve faltered '. . .that is, I assumed. . .that you and Coralie. . .'

'We're friends,' he told her, adding drily, 'Fascinating though your cousin is, I don't play around with married women.'

'Oh,' she said in a small voice. She was somewhat perturbed by the discovery that Ross, who was very charismatic, was not the already booked man she had thought him to be.

His hand at her elbow, he guided her across the street to where the Jaguar stood under a street-lamp. He opened the passenger door for her and she got in. The interior was stylish and comfortable with its burr walnut trim and cream leather seats.

A few seconds later he ducked in alongside her and started the powerful engine. As he pulled out she said, determined not to show that she was still upset by what had happened between her and Trevor, 'Did you know it's forecast that in the rush hour the average speed through London will soon be eleven miles an hour, the roads are so congested?'

'I can tell you read *The Times*,' Ross answered. 'I saw that article too.'

The charm of his smile made her pulse flutter.

Wanting to calm her overtaxed nerves, she opened her clutch bag to find her cigarettes. She shook one out of the packet with nervous fingers and lit it. Her lips trembled slightly as she inhaled.

Blowing out smoke, she said, 'Perhaps the congestion would be eased if. . .' To her dismay her voice choked to a stop.

Ross's mouth tightened with an annoyance that was in no way directed at her. His gaze not leaving the road, he ordered quietly, 'Forget what happened. Trevor was drunk.'

'It doesn't bother me what he said,' she lied fiercely.

'It bothers you very much,' Ross contradicted. He stabbed a keen glance at her. 'Beneath that cool, self-possessed façade, there's a sensitive woman. Just why you're so afraid of letting anyone see that is something I haven't yet fathomed.'

She felt suddenly vulnerable, a feeling she hated.

'Spare me the character analysis, *please*,' she said, turning her sarcasm on him.

'Do you always lash out when you're hurt?'

She turned her head away, struggling with her emotions, and wishing he was less perceptive. 'I've told you,' she insisted in a cramped voice, 'I'm not bothered by what Trevor said.'

'How long have you been going out with him?'

'That's my affair.'

Her even tone robbed her answer of offence while conveying that he was trespassing. Ross gave her a quizzical glance.

'Now you've closed up like a sea-anemone,' he observed.

He read her far too easily and, beginning to snap a little, she said, 'Can we talk about something else?'

'When we've thrashed this out,' he replied. 'Why did you start the evening off by picking a quarrel with Trevor if you're in love with him?'

'I'm not in. . .' she began, then broke off, annoyed that Ross had tripped her into saying out loud something she hadn't wanted to admit to herself.

'Then why are you going out with him?'

'Because I like him,' she retorted.

He gave a soft laugh.

'Poor old Trevor,' he murmured.

Genieve's eyes began to smoulder.

'What do you mean, poor old Trevor?' she demanded. 'Or do you think he was right with what he said about me?'

'That you have a thing against all men in general?' drawled Ross.

Since he was obviously making fun of her she didn't dignify his reply by rising to it. There was a short pause, then he commented, 'You say you like your boyfriend, but if what I saw tonight is typical you walk all over him.'

Strangely, his censure hurt a little.

'Perhaps people get treated the way they deserve,' she said, sweetly sarcastic.

'So you think you deserved to be called frigid?' he said as the Jaguar halted at the lights.

'You would have to bring that up!' she snapped.

'It seemed relevant.'

His reply was accompanied by a brief assessment of her. His gaze admired the curve of her long legs and, instinctively, she moved them, tugging at her hem as she did so. The firm line of his mouth quirked at her action, which proved very nicely that she was far from frigid.

Determined not to lose her temper with him since she was in his debt, she said, 'With Trevor in no fit state to drive, it was nice of you to offer me a lift. But I can do without your comments on my relationship with my boyfriend.'

'I planned to drive you home from the moment I saw you,' Ross said calmly, correcting her assumption.

Her heart seemed to skip a beat. She'd wanted to ignore the magnetism of attraction between them. She still wanted to, despite Ross's statement.

'Why?' she demanded, intending to warn him off with hostility while her skin prickled with awareness.

The traffic lights changed to amber and then green and, as the Jaguar surged forward, he said, 'You know why.' His voice was even, yet there was something intent and telling in it, making her feel almost breathless for an instant. The response of her senses told her that Ross was right. She did know. But she also knew she was terrified of being hurt again. What scared was that deep down was the instinctive comprehension that if she let him, Ross might well threaten her new-found emotional independence.

'You seem to have forgotten, I already have a boyfriend,' she answered coldly, recovering her composure at last, despite the tingling in her blood.

'Trevor?' Ross's voice was lightly scathing. 'Hasn't anyone ever told you that the most disastrous relationships are the ones you just drift into?'

'Not from my experience,' she retorted.

Immediately she felt a blaze of annoyance. Her

statement had revealed far more about herself than she would have wished and, as she had expected, it wasn't lost on Ross. He prompted, 'Which is?'

Refusing to tell him, she said, diverting the conversation, 'Trevor and I may have argued tonight, but in general we get on well together.'

'So well that your relationship is platonic,' Ross pointed out drily.

Furiously she began, 'If you hadn't been eavesdropping. . .'

'I didn't need to eavesdrop,' he cut in. 'You'd have hardly kept flashing me smouldering glances any man could read a mile off if Trevor kept you happy in bed.'

'How dare you?' she spluttered. 'How dare you imply. . .?'

'I dare plenty when I want something,' he returned, cutting her short again, his gaze flickering to her.

A hot little shiver seemed to trace over her skin. She extinguished the cigarette she had just finished and immediately lit another. Hers was a forceful personality, but with Ross she was dealing with a man whose character was even stronger. Becoming more defensive by the minute, she flashed,

'Let me tell you something—I'm an authority on men with your sort of attitude, and there's no way I'm ever getting into a relationship again that's not on my terms and controlled by me!'

She expected him to contest her vehement statement. Instead he observed, 'You smoke too much.'

'What of it?' she said.

'I'd prefer you not to.'

Responding to his request, she stubbed the cigarette

out. As she did so he asked, 'Whereabouts in Harrow do you live?'

She told him, then sat in disquieted silence fingering the rings on her right hand. Now that Ross had stopped making a play for her she felt ashamed of the angry hostility with which she had flared up with him. She didn't want, didn't dare to get involved with him, but she was in his debt, and she could have turned him down in a much nicer fashion.

As the Jaguar purred up the hill she let her eyes stray to his profile. It was clean-cut, his nose patrician, his brows hawkish and his jawline strong and determined. She didn't expect many women had rebuffed him. Yet his face, as she could read it in the faint glow of the dashboard, gave no indication of ill-humour.

'Mine's the end-of-terrace cottage,' she told him in a subdued voice as they approached it. 'I hope I haven't taken you too much out of your way.'

'I live in Loudwater, so no, you haven't,' he answered.

He drew to a smooth halt outside her house and got out to open her door for her. Feeling awkward with him, she collected her clutch bag from the dashboard and got out. As she did so, the rose Andrew had given her fell on to the kerbstone. Ross picked it up.

In his strong tanned fingers it looked delicate, more beautiful. Dangerously aware of the electricity between them, the lateness of the hour, and the enchantment of the soft, still night, Genieve flicked her gaze to his. The chiselled planes of his face were emphasised by the glow of a nearby street-lamp.

'You dropped your rose,' he said, his eyes holding hers.

'I don't want it,' she answered nervously, but took it anyway as he handed it to her. Trying to make amends for the rude way she had rebuffed him, she added, 'I'm sorry if——'

The rest of her sentence was lost as he tilted her chin up to claim her mouth in an ardent-gentle kiss that was over before she had realised his intention.

'I'll call you tomorrow,' he said softly.

She stared at him for an instant. Then, with her heart hammering against her ribs, she fled towards the house. It was only when the front door was safely shut behind her that she paused to catch her breath. She heard the muted roar of the Jaguar engine as Ross pulled away.

Leaning back against the panelled oak door, she pushed back her fringe with unsteady fingers before brushing them against lips that still seemed to feel the sensuous pressure of his mouth on hers. A quiver tremored through her. She was as shaken as if it had been her very first kiss.

'I'll call you,' he had said. All her heated words, telling him that she had no intention of entering into a relationship with him, had gone totally unheeded. Defensive anger welled up inside her. Damn Ross Macauley! He'd have to learn that when she said no, she meant it!

CHAPTER THREE

Genieve awoke to the sound of her clock radio. She had slept fitfully and she felt tired. Puzzled that the news wasn't on, which was her cue to get up, she stirred and looked at the clock. It was only then that she realised the radio must have been playing some time and she had overslept. Dismayed, she threw back the covers. If she was going to be at the boutique by nine o'clock she'd have to hurry.

She drew the curtains, then went into the bathroom and quickly turned on the shower. As the warm water cascaded over her slim body she found she was thinking of her cousin's party. Immediately she was impatient with herself. She had lain awake half the night replaying the events of the previous evening. That was why she had slept through the alarm this morning.

Resolving not to allow Ross to haunt her subconscious any longer, she got dressed. The man was very charismatic and he had an attractive sense of humour, but she found him too disturbing. She wasn't running the risk of being swept off her feet twice. When he called her she was going to make it clear to him that he was wasting his time.

And yet she was glad she had met him, for he had made her realise there was no need for her to worry any more about Paul's letter. Yesterday, jolted by hearing from him out of the blue, she'd been horribly afraid that perhaps her feelings for him weren't dead, that against all her better judgement she'd allow him to persuade her to give their relationship another try now that it was over between him and Vanessa.

Ross had cleared her mind of that misgiving. She couldn't have been so strongly attracted to him, so thrown off balance when he had kissed her goodnight, if she was still in love with Paul Brisbin. Despite his letter saying he wanted them to get back together, she was in no danger of making the same mistakes again with the same man.

She felt her shoulders relax and, stretching like a cat, she crossed over to the window. The playing fields of Harrow School were serene in the pale sunlight. Among the horse-chestnut trees only the faintest tinge of autumn colours showed. It looked as if summer might well linger late into September this year.

The window was slightly open, and she paused a moment, her hand on the catch, reluctant to close it. The air was cool and fresh as though it had been newly rinsed, and somewhere nearby a thrush was singing. A smile tilted the corners of her mouth and she drew a deep breath.

It was as though the morning marked a new beginning for her. She realised that her life was no longer in ruins as she had thought not so long back when she had broken up with Paul. Once he had meant everything to her. Despite her romantic wish to be a virgin for her husband on her wedding night, she had been on the point of compromising her ideals as proof of her love when she had learned of his affair with Vanessa. The memory of his betrayal was still painful enough for her to know that she didn't want to get deeply involved with a man ever again, but, like the survivor of some accident, she had come through.

Gazing out at the green slopes of the hill, she felt a surge of confidence in the future. It was a radiant September morning and the sunshine reflected her more buoyant mood.

She didn't stop for breakfast, but even so the boutique was already open when she arrived. As she locked the door of her Cavalier, she thought how lucky she was to have an assistant who was as dependable as Sherry. She'd been lucky, too, that the boutique had come on the market just at the time when she'd been looking for premises.

It had always been her ambition to set up in business. That was why she had chosen to study economics at university. Afterwards she had gone to work at Harrods. She had enjoyed her job there. Leaving to branch out on her own had been something of a gamble, but it was one which had paid off. Three years on, thanks to her keen management, her fashionable boutique was showing a healthy profit.

Although it was early there was a customer browsing as she walked in. She exchanged a friendly greeting with Sherry, then went through to the small workroom to deal with the post which her assistant had left on her desk. Trade was usually brisk on Saturdays and this one was no exception. There was scarcely a lull all morning.

Sherry had popped out for lunch and Genieve was serving a customer when the shop bell tinkled. She glanced up, surprised to see her cousin entering the boutique.

Seeing that she was busy, Coralie nodded to her and wandered over to a rail of glamorous nightwear.

Genieve smiled back and slipped the two prettily trimmed vests into a carrier bag for her elderly customer.

She guessed that her cousin had spent the morning at the hairdresser's. Not one strand of her burnished french pleat was out of place and her nails were beautifully painted. In a slinky jacket that was softened by a rippling peplum and a short straight skirt she looked feline and sexy.

Obviously she had simply walked out of her apartment that morning, leaving the woman who cleaned for her to clear up the chaos left after the party. That was Coralie all over. Yet, if she was a little thoughtless at times, she was lively company. With her quick wit she made everyone laugh, and Genieve had always found her a good friend.

She was considering a pair of irresistible turquoise silk pyjamas when Genieve's customer left the boutique. Holding the hanger away from her, she announced as the shop door closed, 'You sell some gorgeous things. I simply love these!'

'I've got them in your size if you'd like to try them on,' said Genieve, her eyes playful, because she guessed her cousin had dropped in socially and not to buy.

'Don't tempt me,' Coralie laughed.

'In which case, how about a cup of coffee?'

'No, I mustn't stay. I've got a lunch date.' Coralie opened her handbag and took out a set of car keys. 'I only called in because I happened to be driving out this way, which was just as well, because after I'd packed Trevor off in a taxi last night I realised I'd still got these.'

'Thanks,' said Genieve, her tone a shade wry. 'I'll see he gets them.'

She would post them through his letterbox on her way home, she thought.

'I understand the two of you had a bit of an altercation last night,' her cousin remarked.

'Yes. I'm sorry it happened at your party.'

'Don't be silly,' Coralie protested. 'I wouldn't have known anything about it if Ross hadn't said he was driving you home. Have you finished with Trevor?'

With Ross she'd pretended she hadn't, but with her cousin she was honest. 'Yes, he'd have rung me this morning if he'd wanted to make up.'

'You could always phone him,' Coralie pointed out.

'No. I would rather things had ended between us on a friendlier note, but I don't want to go out with him any more. We were having the most awful scene in your bedroom when Ross came in. I'd no idea he could turn so ugly.'

'I think Ross rather enjoyed rescuing you.' Coralie sounded vaguely amused. She enquired casually, 'Are you seeing him again?'

Genieve shook her head. 'No.'

Once bitten, twice shy, as the saying went. Her romantic friendship with Trevor hadn't worked, and she'd no desire for a deeper relationship with a man. Getting over her broken love affair had been painfully hard, and had she slept with Paul it would have been even harder.

Yet even so a faint prickling seemed to run over her skin as though some premonition warned her. Despite his quick sense of humour and easy manner there was a ruthless persistence about Ross Macauley that scared her a little. If she judged him correctly he wasn't the sort to give up and go away quietly.

Coralie considered her with attentive green eyes.

'You don't sound very convinced.'

'He said he'd call me, but I don't intend getting involved with him.'

Her cousin gave her a smile. 'A wise decision, darling. I know Ross is dynamic and fascinating, but he's not your type.'

'What makes you say that?' Genieve asked, then was cross with herself for asking.

'Intuition,' Coralie stated lightly, hunching her shoulders in a little shrug. 'He's a merchant banker, an absolute wizard with money, and rich as Croesus. But he wouldn't be right for you. He's too flinty. You need someone with more soul.'

Genieve wasn't sure she agreed with her cousin's estimation of Ross. Certainly she could imagine him as a hard-headed pragmatist when it came to business. Behind those hawkish brown eyes was a mind like a precision tool. She wouldn't want to be his opponent in a financial deal, or in anything else.

Yet she sensed that, although he could be ruthless, there was also a sensitive side to his nature. His liking for poetry and art convinced her of that.

'How did you meet him?' she said, allowing him to dominate their conversation in spite of herself.

'Through the gallery. He's a collector.'

'I thought he seemed very knowledgeable about art,' Genieve commented, then said, determined to change the topic, 'You said last night you're off to Hong Kong shortly?'

'Yes, I'm flying out in a fortnight's time. I thought

I'd combine the trip with a couple of weeks' holiday. I'd like to visit Singapore and Penang while I'm out there, so I'll probably be away a month in all.'

'It sounds lovely,' Genieve said with a smile.

'I'm looking forward to it. I hope you're green with envy,' Coralie teased.

They chatted until a customer came in, when Coralie said goodbye. The afternoon wasn't quite as busy as the morning had been, but even so it seemed to fly. Thinking about what she planned to put in the window on Monday, Genieve turned the sign on the door to Closed.

'I hope the weekend's going to stay fine,' her assistant remarked as she came out of the workroom shrugging on her jacket. 'I've let myself be talked into going to watch the stock car racing tomorrow.'

'I thought you liked it.'

'When it doesn't rain,' Sherry agreed. 'The last time we went it poured the whole day. Take my advice, think twice before you marry a sports fan. If he's a real enthusiast he'll think nothing of something trivial like getting soaked to the skin!'

'I'll be warned,' laughed Genieve. 'See you Monday.'

The shop door closed and, as it did, she was conscious of a slight pang of wistfulness. Hearing her assistant talk about her husband with that mixture of humour and affection made her feel strangely lonely for a moment. But she promptly talked herself out of it.

Both her parents were alive. She had two brothers, one in his teens and the other a couple of years younger than herself. She'd left home because of getting a job in London, but hers was still a close-knit family and she had plenty of friends. There was no need to feel lonely.

The way things had ended beween her and Trevor had saddened her a little, that was all.

It was getting on for six when she let herself into her house, her arms full of shopping. She had only just set it down on the kitchen table when the telephone started ringing.

She picked up the receiver, her grip on it tightening as she recognised Ross's charismatic voice.

'Do you like opera?'

She found she was staring at the mouthpiece as though she were staring at the man himself. All day she had been preparing what to say to him if he called her, and now he had thrown her with his first remark.

'I. . .yes. . . What do you mean, do I like opera?' she asked in confusion.

'We're going to see *La Bohème* tonight at the Coliseum,' Ross informed her. 'Is six-thirty too early for me to pick you up?'

'I can't manage tonight. I. . . I already have plans,' she lied, and was thankful he wouldn't know from her answer that her pulse was racing unaccountably.

'Fictitious plans aren't hard to cancel.'

'What makes you think they're fictitious?'

'Aren't they?'

'No,' she answered, clinging to the pretext. 'They're not.'

'No matter. I can get tickets for tomorrow night. Or are you busy then too?' he enquired with a touch of mockery.

'Yes, as it happens.' She tried to sound convincing.

'I guessed as much.' Ross's tone was sardonic. 'Why are you scared to see me again, Genieve?'

The way he said her name made it sound like an

endearment. She felt a quiver trace down her spine in response and, alarmed by the sensation, she answered,

'Don't be ridiculous! Of course I'm not scared of you.'

'That wasn't the impressoin I got last night when I kissed you and you ran for safety,' he returned.

A tinge of colour came into her face. Forgetting that it had been her intention to turn him down politely, she sparked, 'All right, I tried to say no nicely. But since you won't take the hint I'll have to spell it out. I don't wish to go out with you. Now is that too much for you to understand?'

'Not if you'll explain it to me slowly in person,' he jibed, capping her sarcasm. 'I'll see you later.'

He rang off, leaving her feeling confused, angry and more than a little agitated. Returning to the kitchen, she unpacked her shopping, putting the tea into the wrong cupboard and dropping a packet of biscuits on the tiled floor. She picked it up and slapped it on the worktop. Realising the tizzy she was in, she forced herself to calm down.

Why was she letting Ross get her so flustered, she who was always so cool and in control? Disillusioned with love, she had become adept at keeping men at arm's length. It was crazy to think that Ross was somehow different. She had told him she wasn't accepting his invitation and she meant it.

Yet just the same, when the doorbell rang, her heart skipped a beat. Taking a steadying breath, she crossed the sitting-room and opened the front door, knowing it would be Ross.

Her chin lifted as, momentarily arrested by his dark good looks, she stared at him. In a dinner-jacket and black bow tie he was swarthy and urbane, every line and plane of him exuding strength and masculinity. His attire showed just how much notice he had taken of her statement that she wasn't going to see *La Bohème* with him.

His gaze travelled over her, a black eyebrow lifting as he appraised her shapeliness while questioning the simple chemise dress she was wearing.

'Some women like to keep a man waiting,' he began with calm amusement. 'I see you're one of them.'

'I haven't changed because I'm not coming to the theatre with you,' she told him.

He seemed to fill up the doorway with his vitality and the power of his personality. The evening sunlight gleamed on his thick black hair, making it easy for her to imagine she could see midnight blue highlights in it.

'Do I really unsettle you so much that you daren't ask me in?' he mocked.

'You don't unsettle me at all,' she denied, piqued that he had hit on the truth.

'Then why not ask me in?'

'Why should I?'

'Well, for one it would be polite,' he said, amused by her hostility.

Her irresolution lasted no more than a second but, taking advantage of it, he stepped over the threshold before she could stop him. She felt a surge of annoyance. Following him into the sitting-room, she demanded indignantly, 'Do you make a practice of barging into people's houses uninvited?'

'Not usually, no.' His mouth quirked in a reprobate smile. 'But if I'd gone on waiting for you to show a little hospitality I'd probably still be on the doorstep.'

He glanced round, taking note of the bowl of roses on the coffee-table and the William Morris covers on the sofa and armchairs that matched the pleated curtains at the window. 'It's a nice place you've got here,' he commented. 'I like the way you've done it up. It's got style and yet it's homely.'

She couldn't help but be pleased by his approval, though she refused to show it. She knew that her cheeks were flushed and that her pulse was beating too fast, but, determined to fight the polarity of attraction that linked them, she said with a touch of sarcasm, 'I'm glad it meets with your approval. Now, I don't usually kick people out. . .'

'I'm not surprised,' he cut in. 'You haven't got the shoes for it.'

As quick when it came to repartee as he was, she retorted, 'I could always change them.'

'Why not, together with your dress,' he suggested, 'and then, since it's a woman's prerogative, your mind about coming with me to the theatre?'

His easy humour was fast establishing a bond between them that was stronger than her defensive hostility.

'Don't you ever take no for an answer?' she said, a trace of unwilling laughter in her voice.

'What have you to lose?' he teased. One hand came to rest on her shoulder, while the other grazed her cheek in a light caress, making her breath seem to catch in her throat. 'Certainly not your virtue, I promise you.'

Genieve's pulse fluttered. She was aware of his advantage over her in height, of the breadth of his shoulders and the chiselled planes of his strikingly masculine face. Making one last Herculean effort to harden her heart against him, she said, a husky catch in her voice, 'Ross, please. I. . . I like you a lot, but I don't want to go out with you.'

'Give me three good reasons why not.'

'Because. . .' She trailed off, unable to come up with a single explanation that wouldn't be far too telling. Disturbed by his nearness and by the sexual static in the air that was making her heart beat unevenly, she whirled away from him. She took a few paces towards the fireplace, then turned, her hands spread in appeal.

'Look, will you please go away and leave me alone?'

'He really hurt you, didn't he?' said Ross, an abrasive note to his voice.

Her lips parted slightly as she stared into his hard, swarthy face. She couldn't be this transparent, she thought in a panic. How had he managed to guess? Was he able to see everything that went on behind her façade of poise?

She forced herself to relax. Flicking a strand of burnished hair over her shoulder, she asked with a puzzled laugh, 'Trevor?'

Ross smiled thinly at her attempt to create a smoke-screen. He shook his head.

'You didn't love Trevor. You told me so last night, remember?'

Genieve felt herself blush with annoyance. 'Then I don't know who you're talking about,' she said coldly, her eyes that were beginning to spark warning him to leave the subject alone.

'Who was he?' Ross persisted implacably. 'Your fiancé?'

'It's none of your business who he was, or what happened,' she snapped, furious to find that her voice was shaking. She went to walk past him, but he caught hold of her by the arm.

'Don't you think it's time you put it behind you?' he said. His slightly clipped tone revealed that she was trying his patience. 'If you fall in love you know there's a chance you may get hurt. But there are some things in life you can't take out an insurance policy on, relationships being one of them.'

'If I'm so afraid of making another relationship then why did I get involved with Trevor?' she asked defiantly.

'Because you knew you could quell him with a few well chosen words the moment he threatened to get too close. Trevor was no match for you and you knew it.'

'And I suppose you think you are?'

The challenge was stupidly reckless—she realised it the moment she'd spoken. Ross tilted her chin towards him.

'Do you want me to show you?' he taunted, the dangerous silky note in his voice sending prickles of alarm across her skin.

She shied away from him like a nervous filly.

'Don't you dare!' she warned.

As she spoke her heel struck the stone hearth behind her. She stumbled, and Ross's hand shot out. He steadied her and drew her to his chest in one smooth movement.

'Why all the panic?' he mocked softly. 'You've been kissed before, haven't you?'

'You know damn well I have!' she flared. 'Now let go of me!'

She gave a shaken gasp as, instead of complying with her demand, he pulled her even closer. The hardness of his thighs brushed hers, the contact with his powerful man's body making her dizzy. Her heart lurched as she saw his gaze travel to her lips, the tremor of anticipation that went through her robbing her of all strength.

'Ross. . .don't. . .' she pleaded in a helpless whisper.

'Don't what?' he murmured as he bent his head, the strong lines of his face blurring as he kissed her, tasting the sweetness of her lips as though he had all the time in the world and the fierceness of passion could come later.

An acute pleasurable shock went through her, rendering her utterly helpless for an instant. She had known desire before, but never this—never this melting excitement that made her go hot and shaky in response to the lightest of kisses.

Ross raised his head, a somnolent smile glittering in the depths of his eyes as he gazed down at her. For a timeless moment she stared back at him, the air becoming ever more highly charged with knowledge and expectation.

She murmured his name in captivated bewilderment as he bent to her lips again. This time there was no holding back for either of them. It was as though she was meant to be in his possessive arms, as though he was meant to draw from the very soul of her an unclaimed magic.

Their kiss seemed to go on forever, intimate, confessing, insatiable. When finally his mouth left hers, she opened her eyes, her auburn-tipped lashes fluttering up to see him looking down at her. His expression was intent as he noted with masculine satisfaction her altered breathing and the soft fullness of her parted lips.

'That was nice,' he whispered huskily. 'Now hurry up and get changed before I forget the promise I gave you.'

His smile was as shatteringly sensual as his thumb that gently caressed the line of her jaw. Genieve blushed, a flush of heat enveloping her just at the thought of losing what he had teasingly called her virtue to him.

'All. . .all right,' she agreed.

The attractive grooves in his lean cheeks deepened in response to her hurried capitulation.

'Don't be long or we'll be late,' he growled playfully.

'OK,' she said on a breath of laughter, a strange trembling happiness inside her.

Leaving him, she crossed over to the stairs, while he sat down in an armchair, picking up the trade magazine she'd left on the coffee-table. She had almost reached the landing when she paused, her hand on the banisters, to glance down at him. She noted his dark head of hair, his long legs that were stretched out in front of him.

Was it really only yesterday that she had met him? Just as his masculine presence dominated her sitting-room, he seemed to be dominating her life. You're being a fool giving in to his charm, an inner voice warned.

She refused to heed it.

CHAPTER FOUR

THE production was excellent, the poignant human drama finding expression in music that sparkled with merriment one moment, then was eloquent with love, then filled with despair.

'Fantastic!' breathed Ross as the curtain swept down on the final powerful act.

Genieve nodded, too choked with emotion from the last passionate aria to speak. The performance had held the whole house so utterly rapt that it was an instant before the spell broke and the audience began to show its appreciation. Then the applause was thunderous, demanding curtain call after curtain call from a magnificent cast.

When the rapturous and sustained ovation eventually faded and the lights came up, Ross turned to Genieve with a smile.

'Did you enjoy it?'

Her eyes alight, she said, 'Enjoy isn't a strong enough word. It was breathtaking, sheer magic from start to finish.'

'Then you're glad you came,' he grinned roguishly.

She laughed at his teasing, feeling more carefree than she had in months. Moved by the performance, the people in the audience were slow in rising from their seats.

'Let's get ahead of the crush,' Ross suggested.

It was a good idea. They were well on their way out

of the auditorium before the aisles became thronged, slowing their progress.

Ross took her hand as they emerged from the foyer into the warm September night. The traffic was still heavy and plenty of people thronged the pavements. Neon lights flashed intermittently, some proclaiming the theatre shows currently running, others advertising restaurants and coffee shops, but all adding to the firework effect in the velvety darkness.

'How about a meal?' asked Ross, drawing her hand companionably through his arm.

Genieve glanced up at him, seeing the slight challenge in the depths of his eyes and finding that her heart was beating a shade faster. Not knowing why she felt so exhilarated and happy, she answered, 'That would be nice.'

'Then where would you like to go, somewhere quiet and intimate, or somewhere lively and crowded?'

She hesitated an instant, then decided that candlelight and soft music weren't to be trusted.

'Somewhere lively and crowded,' she stated.

'I thought you might say that,' mocked Ross, arching a knowing eyebrow at her.

She coloured a little but was quick to come back with a quip.

'I'm a lively person.'

'Lively, complex and bewitching,' he murmured in reply.

The sensual note in his voice left her in no doubt that he was very attracted to her.

The nightclub he drove them to was one she hadn't been to before, though she knew it was a favourite with her cousin. The panelled reception hall was quiet, unlike the downstairs that was full of people and noise with the disco throbbing, and members shrieking cheerfully to each other on their way to the laser-lit dance floor.

'When you said somewhere lively and crowded you weren't joking!' Genieve laughed.

'We'll try the quiet and intimate bit later,' Ross said, a wicked glint in his dark eyes.

She glanced away, partly to conceal the mercurial rise of her pulse, and partly to survey the décor. Colonial-style brass fans whirred on the ceiling, adding to the nightclub's sophisticated charm. The smoked mirror glass behind the bar reflected bursts of greenery and chrome and red leather chairs. Genieve glimpsed a number of famous faces among the ultra-fashionably dressed clientele.

They themselves didn't go unnoticed as they were promptly shown to a well-placed table. Several of the women eyed Ross with undisguised interest, and Genieve with a touch of envy. The two of them made a striking couple. In a peacock-blue evening dress with a strapless bodice and skirts of chiffon and silk, she had all the poise and grace of a dancer, while Ross, with his powerful man's physique and dark good looks, was the perfect foil to show her off.

'You certainly know how to do things in style,' she said some while later, laughter in her voice. 'Is this the way you usually relax?'

'You find this place relaxing!' His smile was humorous and she returned it without thinking, her blue eyes sparkling attractively. 'To relax I usually play a round of golf or have a game of squash,' he told her. 'Nightclubs and champagne are for when I want to sweep a particularly elusive redhead off her feet.'

She gave him a slightly guarded look from under her lashes and he raised an ironic eyebrow.

'Worried I might succeed?' he mocked.

She was, a little, but, picking up her glass, she said with engaging defiance, 'You can try.'

'Meaning that you intend keeping your feet firmly on the ground,' he summarised, as though amused by her independence.

'Very firmly,' she informed him as she looked at his strikingly masculine face.

It was a very strong face, the character that was stamped in each chiselled feature telling her that he was a man who was single-minded when it came to getting what he wanted. One glance at him was enough to know that he would be an expert lover, gentle, passionate, tender. Alarmed by the wayward direction her thoughts had taken, she flushed slightly.

'What's going on now behind those enigmatic blue eyes of yours?' Ross challenged.

Genieve shook her head. 'Let's talk about you,' she said. 'You haven't told me very much about yourself.'

'What do you want to know?'

'Well, to start with, are you married, single, divorced?' Though she framed the question flippantly she felt cold suddenly. She'd assumed Ross was unattached, but she might be wrong, and she didn't want to be disillusioned.

'Do I act like a married man?' he said drily.

'It's not always possible to deduce anything from the way a man acts. You could be separated.'

'In which case, to set your mind at rest, I'm single.'

'Have I offended you?'

'By asking me if I'm married? No, I'm not offended,'

he said, 'just sorry you seem to have such a low opinion of men in general. The influence of your erstwhile lover, I take it.'

She knew she had earned the sardonic comment. Fingering the stem of her glass, she said, 'Paul wasn't married, if that's the conclusion you've jumped to. He. . .he didn't believe in the institution.'

'Then he's different from me.'

The usual trace of masculine humour was back in his voice and, raising her gaze to his, she said with a smile, 'If that's true, why are you single?'

'Till now I've enjoyed playing the field.'

'Till now?' she queried, not sure if she understood him correctly and somehow compelled to ask.

'Are you wondering where you stand with me?' he drawled, the lazy gleam in his eyes sending a shiver tracing down her spine.

'Is that what you'd like me to be thinking?' she countered defiantly, totally unaware of the way his interest in her brought the lovely lines of her face alive.

'Yes,' he said frankly, his smile far too attractive.

An apricot blush crept into her cheeks. When she'd flirted with other men it had always been a game, but flirting with Ross was somehow spiced with danger.

'I never thought I'd see you at a loss for an answer,' he teased.

'It must be the champagne,' she said with a laugh, reaching for her cigarettes.

Before she could shake one out of the packet, he took hold of her hand.

'Let's dance,' he said.

'I get the feeling you don't like me smoking.'

'I've told you—you smoke too much,' he said as he led her through the tables to the crowded dance floor.

While they had lingered over their meal the disco beat had changed to a slower tempo. Ross drew her close and a quiver went through her in response to feeling his hard body so close to hers.

She saw him nod to a good-looking, well-dressed woman at a nearby table.

'A client,' he explained. His mouth quirked slightly as he went on. 'She's Greek, a rich widow with a shipping empire. We're currently financing the three bulk carriers she's having built in Gdansk. Convinced now?'

'Why should I need convincing?'

'Because you seem to have me typecast as a playboy,' he said, his eyes teasing her.

Genieve smiled back, feeling happy and a little dizzy. Was it a result of the cold heady wine or the effect of Ross's charm? His magnetism was powerful and she was more than half bewitched by the romance of the evening.

The rhythm of the music spun its silken thread about them, uniting them as they danced together, making the other couples on the crowded floor seem to retreat like so many shadows. She had never known dancing to be such a sensual experience. Her blood seemed to tingle as Ross's hand caressed her back.

'I don't know much about merchant banking,' she murmured. 'What do you do, apart from investing people's money in stocks and shares?'

'We finance innumerable ventures. A few months ago I was in Rome looking into the viability of under-writing a major European bond issue. Last week I was in New York for a meeting with the directors of the bank's American subsidiary. Now I'm handling a new share flotation for a company that's decided to go public next year.'

'It all sounds very high-powered,' Genieve said, a little in awe of him.

Now she understood why he had such an air of authority and self-possession. A part of the hard, swift-moving business world, he was a man who took decisions fast and followed them up with prompt action.

They were returning to their table when she noticed her cousin seated not far off.

'Oh, look, there's Coralie!' she exclaimed in surprise. 'And Geoff's with her.'

'Who's Geoff? Another boyfriend?' Ross asked her.

'He's her husband, but they've gone their separate ways for some time now.'

'Do you want to go over and say hello?'

Despite the easy way he spoke, she sensed he was reluctant to have anyone intrude on their intimate twosome. She felt the same, but at that moment Geoff recognised her and smiled in greeting.

'We'll have to,' she said. 'They've seen us.'

Coralie looked stunning in a black evening dress that was daringly slashed practically to the last vertebra of her spine. She glanced up, something flickering in the depths of her green eyes as she saw Ross, attractive and urbane, at Genieve's side.

The introduction between the two men completed, Geoff, laconic and friendly as ever, insisted that Genieve and Ross join them. As he signalled to the waiter for more drinks Coralie said, amusement in her light, flexible voice. 'Well, aren't you just a dark horse, Genieve?'

Ross arched a black eyebrow. 'In what way a dark horse?'

'My little cousin gave me the impression she wasn't going to see you again.'

'Indeed?'

He glanced at Genieve and, responding to the roguish tilt of his mouth, she smiled back and said laughingly, 'Ross was very persuasive.'

The four of them talked together until Geoff asked Genieve to dance. The nightclub had filled up still more, although it was now well past one o'clock, and, since there was little room on the floor, they stayed on the edge of it.

'I was surprised to see you here with Coralie,' Genieve said as she linked her arms behind Geoff's neck.

'Yes, I can imagine. My wife and I haven't exactly been on speaking terms of late,' he answered, irony in his tone as he looked beyond her to where Coralie sat, poised and slim, one elbow resting lightly on the table, an elegant hand beneath her chin as she chatted to Ross.

Noting the direction of his gaze, Genieve asked, 'Do you still love her, Geoff?'

'What an incurable romantic you are!' he mocked.

She laughed and said, 'Is it being a romantic to want to see two people I like very much get back together?'

Geoff shook his head. 'There's not much chance of that, I'm afraid.'

'Then. . .then what are the two of you doing here tonight?'

'Discussing a divorce,' he said drily.

'But I thought. . . I thought you were against the idea?'

'I am,' he agreed. 'I've told Coralie that if she wants a divorce, she'll have to file the petition.'

'She can't. You've given her no grounds.'

'Precisely, which means the way the law stands at the moment, she'll have to wait till we've been separated five years before she can end our marriage.'

'I was right, wasn't I?' Genieve said. 'You do still love her.'

'Because I won't give her the divorce she wants?'

She nodded and he said with a hard smile, 'Maybe I just want to even the score a little after the dance she's led me.'

'Maybe,' Genieve murmured sceptically, knowing him better than that.

Despite her loyalty to her cousin, she felt a faint stir of exasperation with her. Why ever didn't Coralie realise what she was throwing away by turning her back on what could have been a strong marriage?

'I think it's time you danced with me now,' said Ross as she returned to her place.

'The floor's very crowded,' she answered, a mischievous light in her eyes.

Amused by her teasing defiance, he took hold of her hand and said, 'Then I'll just have to hold you very tight, won't I?'

Genieve laughed—then gave a little gasp as Coralie's glass went over on the table, spilling its contents in her lap.

'Oh, how could I be so clumsy?' her cousin wailed in apology. 'Is your dress ruined?'

Ross quickly passed Genieve his handkerchief.

'I expect it will come out,' she said, hoping that it would as she mopped up the vodka and lime.

In the ladies' room she dabbed the stain with cold water. She was inspecting her chiffon skirt to see if she'd succeeded in getting it out when her cousin came in.

Giving Genieve a cursory glance, she asked, 'Has it left a mark?'

'No, I don't think so.'

'If it had it would have been no great loss,' her cousin remarked dismissively. 'From the looks of it, your dress didn't cost much in the first place.'

'Thanks!' Genieve exclaimed, indignant laughter in her voice.

'Pleasure!' Slender shoulders hunched in a tiny shrug. 'So what are you doing here with Ross tonight?'

'We went to the opera and then came on for dinner.'

'Nice work, darling,' her cousin applauded, giving her a cold little smile as she checked her make-up in the long mirror. 'I suppose you'd already decided you preferred Ross to Trevor when you dumped him at my party.'

'Trevor was drunk,' Genieve protested, her blue eyes beginning to spark. 'What happened between us had nothing to do with Ross.'

Coralie slipped her lipstick back in her bag. 'Well, let's hope you have more luck with him than you did with the last man I introduced you to,' she said carelessly. 'Still, better to be stood up after a couple of dates than to be jilted after a year and a half.'

'What the hell's got into you tonight?' Genieve demanded angrily, stung by the most spiteful remark yet.

'Nothing's got into me,' Coralie flashed back. 'I just don't want to see you get hurt, that's all.'

'What makes you think I'll get hurt with Ross?'

'You're out of your depth with him. He may find your ingénue charm interesting for one evening, but he's worldly-wise and almost ten years older than you are. I doubt very much. . .'

'Will you stop treating me as if I'm a schoolgirl?' Genieve cut in. 'I'm quite capable of looking after myself.'

'Just don't come running to me when it all ends in disaster,' Coralie said bitingly. 'You couldn't hold on to Paul, and you certainly haven't got what it takes to keep a man like Ross satisfied for long.'

'Have you finished?' asked Genieve, an edge to her voice.

'I haven't started yet!' her cousin retorted, then checked herself with an angry breath. 'I'm sorry,' she apologised. 'I'm being a real bitch tonight. It's Geoff—he's put me in a filthy mood. He brings out the very worst in me at times.'

The stormy light faded from Genieve's eyes. Accepting the olive branch, she said with a touch of humour, 'So I'd noticed!'

'I was a fool not to deal with him through my solicitor,' her cousin said. 'I should have known he'd be unreasonable.'

'Isn't there a chance the two of you could put things right?' Genieve asked. 'I'm sure he still cares about you.'

'When I need your advice I'll ask for it. OK?'

'I was only trying to. . .'

'Well, don't,' Coralie snapped.

With that she swept out. Genieve sighed shortly, finished neatening her hair, then returned to their table.

'It's time you and I made a move,' Ross said a short while later, glancing at his watch.

After the music and the buzz of conversation, the night seemed calm and peaceful, the sky that was sprinkled with stars forming an inky backdrop to pavements that were golden in the glow of the street lamps.

'Why so quiet suddenly?' Ross asked, as with her hand tucked through his arm they strolled to his car.

'I was thinking about Coralie. She's more upset than she shows about the break-up of her marriage.'

'Forget your cousin,' Ross ordered. 'You've got enough to concentrate on with me.'

'That's a little callous, isn't it?' Genieve challenged as they halted by his Jaguar.

'Your cousin's a born survivor,' he said, tracing the outline of her cheek with his strong clever fingers before tilting her chin up imperiously. He brushed the tender line of her mouth with his thumb. 'You, on the other hand, despite your wilful ways, are warm-hearted and very. . .very. . .sweet.'

The last was said in a hypnotic murmur as he bent his head to claim her lips in a slow lingering kiss.

Genieve's heart jolted wildly. Though the only contact between them was where their mouths met and his hand shaped her face, pleasure licked like fire along her veins.

'I can't think straight when you kiss me like that,' she said, her voice a breathless whisper as his lips left hers.

'Perhaps that's what I want,' he said, the charm of his smile sending a shock wave through her.

The Jaguar was hemmed in by other cars. Ross eased

it smoothly out of the tight space. She glanced at his craggy profile, noting the patrician line of his nose, his hawkish brows. He was alert, amusing, caustic and imperturbable.

The passionate love duet from Act One of *La Bohème* was running through her head, and softly she sang a snatch of it. Ross slanted a glance at her and smiled. 'I'm glad you enjoy opera. It's a good interest to share.'

'I wouldn't say I enjoy all opera. I find Wagner a bit heavy going,' she admitted.

'Which are your favourites?'

'I like *Carmen* very much, and *Madam Butterfly*. *The Tales of Hoffmann* is lovely too. I'm afraid I'm not a highbrow,' she joked.

'Why be afraid about it?' Ross asked, amused.

His question started a discussion about music which lasted until the shadowy outline of Harrow Hill, with the spire of St Mary's rising above the trees, came into view, silhouetted against the dark sky. Far too soon for Genieve, the Jaguar drew to a halt outside her cottage.

'I've had the nicest evening,' she said, then hesitated an instant. She'd made a number of resolutions where Ross was concerned, but having broken each one in turn, she saw little point in keeping rigidly to the last. 'Would you. . .would you like to come in for coffee, or perhaps a nightcap?'

'Thanks,' he accepted, 'I would.'

Her sitting-room seemed even more cosy and intimate now it was so late. She turned on the lamp by the hearth and, with its soft light playing on her burnished hair, hunted in the corner cupboard.

'Brandy or sloe gin?' she asked, then apologised with a smile, 'I'm sorry I haven't got much to offer you.'

Ross's dark eyes glinted, his gaze travelling deliberately from the perfection of her features to the lovely lines of her throat and shoulders. She drew a sharp intake of breath, her blood tingling from the insolent caress of his gaze.

'I wouldn't say that,' he murmured.

Pretending she had missed the innuendo, Genieve left it to him to pour the drinks. Her heart was beating much too quickly. Intuitively she knew Ross hadn't misunderstood her when she'd invited him in. He wasn't going to try to make a move to get her into bed, yet even so the air seemed to vibrate with undercurrents of excitement, danger and expectation.

Not understanding them, she took her drink and sat down with it on the edge of an armchair. Her eyes downcast, she studied the ruby-red liqueur in her glass before confessing, 'When you showed up here this evening I promised myself I'd be so cool and flippant.'

'And now?'

His charismatic voice was shaded with speculation. She raised her gaze to look at where he sat across the room from her, nursing his brandy, the glow from the standard lamp accentuating the chiselled planes of his alert swarthy face. In his dark dinner jacket he was urbane, yet even evening attire couldn't blunt the raw predatory quality of his masculinity.

As she realised how powerfully she was drawn to him, a wave of uncertainty rocked her. Ross was an emotional storm, an unknown force sweeping into her tranquil life and shattering common sense to fragments.

'I don't know,' she faltered. 'I've never met anyone

like you before. I thought it was the champagne that
was making me giddy and unsure. Now I think it's you,
and it frightens me.'

'Why should it frighten you?' he asked, coming to
perch on the arm of her chair.

He ran a gently caressing hand along her naked
shoulder and, alarmed by the shiver of response that
went through her, she got swiftly to her feet.

'Because I swore I'd never feel like this again.' She
turned back to him, her agitated confusion giving way
to a flash of anger as she saw him smile. 'What's funny
about that?' she flared defensively.

'Nothing's funny,' he told her. He stood up and
taking hold of her lazily by the wrist, pulled her towards
him. 'I just didn't think the gods could be this kind.'

His superior height forced her to look up at him. In
every inch of her she seemed aware of the ruggedness
and virility that were stamped in his physique, of the
powerful awareness that pulsed between them. He
made her feel weak, feminine and unweaponed. Fear
of those feelings prompted her to be all the more fiery.

'What are you talking about?' she demanded, before
insisting, 'And will you let go of me!'

Ross shook his head. With arrogant firmness he drew
her into his embrace.

'You're going to have to get used to being in my
arms,' he answered.

'Oh?' she said, feeling very breathless suddenly.
'Why?'

'Do you really need me to tell you?' Ross returned
with a touch of irony.

'I suppose you've decided we're destined to become
lovers,' she challenged.

'What I've decided is that we're going to get married.'

CHAPTER FIVE

GENIEVE stared at him, her lips parted. Breathless and confounded, she took a moment before she could recover enough to stammer, 'Are you. . .are you crazy?'

'No, and I'm not joking either,' Ross stated, guessing what she was about to say next.

'But. . .but we hadn't even met until yesterday!' she exclaimed, her dazed mind struggling to assimilate the fact that he was actually proposing to her.

'How long does it take to fall in love?' he challenged. Steady force behind his words, he went on, 'I knew I wanted you the instant I saw you.'

His gaze held hers as he spoke, the lambent desire she saw smouldering in the depths of his hard expressive eyes making her heart beat unevenly. There was no doubt about it. He meant what he said.

She drew breath to murmur his name, only to have the next devastating realisation crash in on her. She had built what she'd thought was an impregnable wall around her feelings. Now that wall, so carefully constructed, so carefully guarded, lay all but in ruins. Thrown into turmoil by the knowledge, she pushed hard but ineffectually at his rock-like shoulders.

'I won't believe you're serious!' she declared, a hint of panic in her voice.

'Then maybe it's time I showed you I am.'

She tried to hit out at him as he bent his head, her

67

hand that was balled into a fist unclenching to clutch at his jacket as his mouth claimed hers in a searching, almost shockingly passionate kiss. She had meant to resist him. Instead, as his firm, insistent mouth parted her lips, sending wild tremors dancing along her nerves, she dug her fingers into his back, clinging to him as though he were the only stable force in a dizzily swaying world. His jacket was open and, through his crisply pleated shirt, the live heat of his body spread to hers, tantalising her breasts.

His mouth was exploring hers with demanding thoroughness, his darting tongue making her groan against his lips. On fire with longing, she tipped her head back, surrendering completely to the invasion of his kiss.

It was only when he brought his hands down, letting her feel his arousal, that the insanity of what she was allowing hit her. She was telling him everything with the ardency of her response. Turning her head away, she broke the kiss, her face flushed, her body trembling and feverish.

Genieve. . .' He muttered her name, his mouth sliding to her neck.

An agonising dart of pleasure went through her as he pressed his lips to her throat.

'No more. . .' she moaned raggedly. 'Ross, please. . .'

He kissed her once more, then raised his head.

'Say yes,' he murmured, his thumb caressing her cheek. 'Say yes, you'll marry me.'

She opened her eyes to see the dark commanding glitter in his. She could feel the rise and fall of his deep chest. The touch of his strong, gentle hand was achingly sweet. Before she had even thought, she whispered the word he wanted to hear.

He drew a quick breath as she spoke and, realising suddenly what she had promised, she gasped,

'I mean—I don't know. Stop. . .stop confusing me like this!'

The attractive line of Ross's mouth quirked. Amusement tempering the desire that still burned in his eyes, he said, 'Your first answer was fine.'

'I didn't mean to say it,' she insisted, trying to break free from his arms, which he wouldn't allow.

'The power of the subconscious mind,' he mocked. 'OK, if you need more time to make sure of your feelings, my blue-eyed witch, I'm prepared to wait.'

She gazed up at him, her pulse racing. She had to put a stop to this. To fall in love again had been the very thing she'd been determined would never happen.

'I don't intend getting married,' she stated huskily.

Ross raised a sardonic eyebrow. 'Ever?' he queried. The strong lines of his face softened as his teasing coaxed a smile out of her. 'I realise I've taken you by surprise,' he went on, a trace of roguishness in his voice as he said, 'but I think you might enjoy being married to me.'

Her blush confirmed that his insinuation was far from lost on her. She pushed at his shoulders and this time he released her. The power of his charisma and the magnetism between them were such that for a fleeting moment she was strongly tempted to agree to be his wife and to disregard the fact that until yesterday they'd been strangers.

She took a couple of steps away from him, putting

her hands to her temples in an attempt to recover her grip on reality.

'This is a ridiculous discussion!' she exclaimed.

'You only think that because you're afraid to take a chance.'

'That's not true!'

'Isn't it?' He turned her towards him. She saw the purposeful set of his jaw and then his face relaxed. With a sigh he reached out to tuck a strand of silken hair behind her ear. 'You're so beautiful,' he murmured. 'Come out with me tomorrow. We'll have lunch together somewhere and talk about the two of us.'

'Oh, Ross. . .'

'Tell me you'll come.'

Genieve gave a slight nod and he said, the grooves deepening on either side of his attractive mouth, 'Just think, we could have an autumn wedding.'

Afraid he would see the inner conflict that was mirrored in her eyes, she dropped her gaze. Ross moved to the front door, tall and powerful, a panther's grace in his lithe step.

'Sleep on the idea,' he advised, serious for all the good humour in his voice.

'Ross. . .' She stopped him as he opened the door.

'Yes?'

'I. . .' She broke off, not knowing why she had spoken or what she had intended to say. She hesitated and then, obeying an impulse stronger than herself, she went towards him, sliding her arms around his neck as she stood on tiptoe to kiss him fleetingly on the lips. Her heartbeat quickened, she drew back and whispered unsteadily, 'Goodnight.'

He brushed her cheek in a light caress.

'Goodnight, sweetheart,' he returned softly. 'I'll call you in the morning.'

She stood for a moment staring after his tall figure and then, as he ducked into his Jaguar, she closed the door. She heard the muted roar as he started the car and then its smooth purr as it pulled away, the sound eventually fading, swallowed up in the vast silence of the night.

An expression of unfathomable wonder in the depths of her eyes, she wandered into the centre of the room. She hugged her arms, trying her best to be sensible against the trembling feeling of happiness inside it.

It was crazy his asking her to marry him, just as she had said. And yet. . . And yet with his firm personality and masculine charisma he affected her more powerfully than any man she'd ever met. She had promised herself that she wouldn't get involved with him, and he had made nonsense of that promise.

Her thoughts in a whirl, she went upstairs and got ready for bed. Despite her resolve to hold on to her independence, deep down was the feeling that Ross represented some kind of destiny for her. The question was whether she was ready to take a chance on love again.

Seeing his hard masculine face in her mind, she snuggled under the duvet, expecting another restless night after such a maelstrom of an evening. Instead, deep luxurious sleep claimed her almost immediately, her last conscious thought the memory of the way he had kissed her.

It was late in the morning when she stirred drowsily. She stretched her legs towards the end of the bed,

wondering why she felt so good, and then she remembered. It had not been a dream. Ross had said he
wanted to marry her.

Debating what to wear for her lunch date with him,
she slipped on her silk wrap. As she did so she caught
sight of her reflection in the dressing-table mirror. Her
burnished hair was gathered softly behind her neck,
framing a face made beautiful by a kind of inner
radiance. The misty glow in her eyes startled her.

Was it thinking about Ross that made her look this
way? His proposal had made her feel as if she were
standing on the threshold of some magic doorway. But
did she dare take the step to discover what lay beyond?
Her heart told her, yes, take it; her head said, wait.

What was the rush? she rationalised. Ross had said
he'd give her time to make sure of her feelings, so why
not delay her answer until she was certain, and in the
meantime simply enjoy his company and their
courtship?

At that moment the phone rang. Thinking it would
be Ross, she ran downstairs to answer it. She picked up
the receiver, then smiled, even though it wasn't the call
she had been expecting.

'Mother!' she exclaimed. 'How nice to hear you!'

'Hello, darling. You sound very happy this morning!'

'Do I?' she sparkled. She debated mentioning Ross
and then decided she wasn't ready to share her feelings
about him with anyone yet. 'How's everything at home?
I'm looking forward to driving down for the weekend
on Saturday.'

'That's why I'm ringing, to remind you,' her mother
teased.

'I don't need reminding,' Genieve laughed. 'I couldn't forget Dad's birthday.'

'You know we're planning a party for him, don't you? So do bring a friend. It's no trouble to put an extra visitor up. Your brother's coming from Cambridge with his girlfriend, so they'll be staying overnight too.'

There was the sound of Richard Dearing's good-tempered voice in the background.

'What's Dad saying?' Genieve smiled, hearing her mother laugh.

'He says he can't believe he'll be sixty in a few days' time. He doesn't feel it.'

'Sixty's not old,' Genieve protested. 'Anyway, he must be one of the most energetic vets in Gloucestershire.'

'He was working till all hours yesterday,' her mother told her, going on to describe how he had been called out late by a local farmer to attend a sick calf.

'Let's hope he won't be called out next Saturday,' said Genieve. 'How many people are coming to the party?'

'About forty, so I'm planning a buffet. By the way, Coralie tells me she'll be in Bristol on Friday on business, which means she'll be coming after all.'

'Would you like me to try to get home a day early so I can help you with the preparations?' Genieve asked.

'No, dear, that's sweet of you, but everything's in hand,' her mother answered. 'Come at whatever time suits you.'

Their conversation drew to a close, and Genieve had only just hung up when the phone rang again.

'How's my fiancée this morning?' Ross's voice, smooth and dark as liquid chocolate, was like a caress.

'I didn't. . .' Genieve began, far more breathlessly than she'd greeted her mother, although this time she hadn't had to speed downstairs to answer the phone.

'I know you didn't,' Ross cut in, 'but you did say you'd have lunch with me. Shall I pick you up in about half an hour?'

'I'll try not to keep you waiting this time,' she said playfully as she alluded to the previous evening.

'Don't tell me you've only just got up?' he mocked.

'Well, it was quite a night last night.'

'It was at that,' he agreed softly.

The hotel he drove them to was just outside Beaconsfield. Set well back from the road with a wide frontage, it was elegant and had a welcomng atmosphere. They sat in the restaurant lounge to consider the menu over an aperitif.

Just as on the previous evening Ross made her laugh, setting her at ease and amusing her. It wasn't until the waiter came up to take their order that she realised she'd scarcely glanced at the menu. Her attention had been entirely focused on Ross.

'What will you have?' he asked, smiling at her.

Deciding quickly, she said, 'I'd like the noisettes of lamb.'

They were shown through into the restaurant to a table with a lovely view over the hotel's grounds. To accompany their meal Ross chose a Château Lynch-Bages vintage claret. Genieve's pensive gaze lingered on him as the wine waiter presented him with the bottle and uncorked it.

Until now she'd never believed she'd fall in love a

second time. Or she'd thought that, if she did, it would be to discover a gentle, secure type of love. She'd been badly hurt by one highly charged relationship. She didn't want to be caught up in another.

And yet, with Ross, what other kind of relationship was possible? A flash of panic seemed to go through her with the thought. Forceful and charismatic, he was a man to take control and to dominate, the very sort of man she'd sworn she'd never get involved with again. So what on earth was she doing seriously considering his proposal?

Yet even as she asked herself the question she knew the answer, just as she knew why the air seemed to vibrate between them at times. Ross raised his glass to his lips and she watched as, having warmed the wine in his mouth, he swallowed, strong throat muscles flexing with the movement. A hot prickling ran over her skin and, slightly shocked by the flush of sexual awareness, she dropped her gaze.

'Excellent,' Ross complimented the wine waiter, who filled their glasses with a pleased flourish and withdrew.

Absently Genieve sipped her wine.

'Why so serious suddenly?' Ross's voice, lightly shaded with humour, made her glance up.

With no intention of being drawn on what she'd been thinking, she smiled and said, 'I always look serious when I'm judging a good claret.'

Ross laughed, and the mood was set for an enjoyable, undemanding lunch. The service was attentive and unhurried, while the quiet murmur of conversation from the other tables drifted by unnoticed. They talked about various things as they ate, delving into politics and current affairs, then touching on travel and other lighter topics.

Ross was interested in hearing about her plans for the boutique. His keen, dark eyes considering, he listened as she spoke about her aim of having several outlets eventually.

'That's why I'm going on a management course in November,' she told him. 'It's very short, only four days, but it's intensive and specifically tailored for small businesses in the process of expanding. I think it will be time well invested.'

Ross quirked an eyebrow at her in mock tribute.

'You're an ambitious lady.'

'I like a challenge,' she said, engaging bravado in her smile.

'Well, well!'

His dark eyes glinted and she felt her pulse quicken. It was the very element of danger that made flirting with Ross exciting. But what if the danger should get out of hand? She was trying to keep her head where he was concerned.

She moistened her lips and said, simply for the sake of trying to subdue her awareness of the static in the air, 'It's three years since I started the boutique. Now that it's doing well some of the stimulus of meeting difficulties is over, so I need something new to act as a spur. That spur's another shop, then another. But, much as I hope to expand, I wouldn't want the business ever to take over to the exclusion of all else.'

'What other things are important to you?' asked Ross.

'A home life.'

'You mean children?'

In the light of his proposal his statement took on a significance which made her blush.

'I. . .yes. . .eventually.'

'Good, then that's something else we have in common,' he said, taking hold of her hand across the table.

His touch and the lazy intimacy of his dark eyes played havoc with her senses. She felt his thumb brush over her knuckles in a caress and, conscious of the warmth in her face, she made to withdraw her hand. But Ross forestalled her. Threading his fingers through hers, he said with a touch of amusement, 'You blush very prettily.'

'You're making fun of me!' she protested.

'Only gently,' he assured her, before saying quietly, taking her by surprise, 'Tell me about the man who hurt you.'

'We. . .we met one day when I dropped in at the gallery,' she faltered. 'It was the start of a stormy romance that lasted about a year and a half. That's all there is to tell.'

'Why did the two of you split up?' Ross asked evenly, his dark eyes commanding hers.

'A friend of Coralie's told me he was two-timing me.' Strangely, it was easier than she'd expected to talk about it. She went on, 'I always thought Alice enjoyed being spiteful. I refused to believe her, but I suppose I wanted reassurance because I told him what she'd said. That was when I found out it was true. Paul. . . Paul said he'd never given me any promises. He was free to date or sleep with anyone he wanted.' Ross's mouth tightened and Genieve said immediately, 'It was my own fault I got hurt. If I'd used an ounce of common

sense I'd have seen it was inevitable we'd break up
sooner or later.'

Ross was silent, studying her with an unfathomable
intensity, and she wondered if she should tell him she
was no longer in love with Paul, before realising it
would be stating the obvious. It must be plain to him
that she wouldn't be thinking of being his wife if she
was in love with someone else.

Paul belonged to the past, and yet what worried her
was that a year ago she had had none of the insight into
their relationship she had now. She'd been too emotion-
ally involved to see Paul as he really was. And that
frightened her, because in her heart she knew she was
still the same romantic.

She looked into Ross's rugged face. She wanted to
trust her feelings where he was concerned, but she'd
trusted them once before, only to be hurt and disillusioned. To remember Paul was always to be filled with
a sense of insecurity. She knew very little about Ross.
Surely she was right to be taking things slowly?

Their waiter arrived to serve them with coffee. Rich
and aromatic, it rounded off the meal perfectly.

'What made you decide to go in for banking?' she
asked Ross as she helped herself to a wafer-thin mint.

'I was going to be a professional tennis player or an
airline pilot till I was fourteen,' he joked.

'What happened?' she laughed.

'My father died,' he told her. 'My mother had died a
couple of years before, so I went to live with an uncle.
He suggested I should think about banking. The idea
gradually took hold, and those of playing at Wimbledon
or piloting Concorde faded.'

Though he didn't say as much, Genieve guessed his

childhood had been lonely. His was a strong character and a complex one, the hard, ruthless side of his nature balanced by a gentleness that was all the more appealing because in him it was such a masculine quality.

They were still lingering over coffee when she said on a sigh of contentment, 'I've really enjoyed it here.'

'Then let's come back on Saturday for dinner.'

'I'll be in Gloucestershire on Saturday,' she told him. 'It's my father's birthday and my mother's giving a party for him. I . . . I was wondering if you'd like to come too.'

'You mean to meet your parents,' he surmised, teasing her with a wickedly attractive smile. 'I'd like to come very much.'

The party at her parents' home was in sharp contrast to the brittle, sophisticated affair thrown by her cousin where she had met Ross. A log fire burned cheerfully in the large drawing-room where some of the guests sat chatting, while the double doors were open on to the hall and to the dining-room beyond, where more talk and laughter abounded.

Most people had now served themselves from the buffet, but the cake, which was placed in the centre of the table, hadn't yet been cut. In preparation for the moment, glasses of champagne were being handed round among the guests.

Hurriedly Genieve turned to Ross.

'I must get some photos of Dad cutting the cake,' she said, quickly handing him her drink.

She sped from the room, feeling his look of masculine amusement between her shoulder blades as she went out. In the doorway she collided with the elder of her two brothers.

'Sorry, Clive,' she laughed, clutching hold of him to steady herself.

'What's happened?' he said urgently. 'Where's the fire?'

'Very funny,' she joked back. 'I'm dashing to get my camera. Dad's about to cut the cake.'

'Don't worry, I'll see the action doesn't start without you,' Clive said as she slipped past him into the hall.

'Thanks,' she called back.

She'd left her camera on the desk in the study. She was checking the number of shots she'd got left when her cousin came in with a whisper of silk chiffon.

Her black three-piece was extremely chic. Shot with glittering silver thread, it showed off her chestnut hair and porcelain skin to perfection while lending a sultry darkness to her eyes.

She always manages to look so sexy, Genieve thought a shade wistfully, unaware of the subtle potency of her own allure. Her bias-cut dress of indigo crêpe suited her well, giving depth to her colouring, the clinging fabric flattering her figure without sensationalising it.

'I was hoping to get a minute to talk to you alone,' Coralie began, the inflexion of her voice suggesting she had some exciting secret to share.

'What about?' asked Genieve, wondering if she was about to announce that she had decided to give her marriage another try.

Coralie circled the desk and sat down in the leather-upholstered chair behind it. Fingering the glass paper-weight in front of her, she said, deliberately being mysterious, 'I had a phone call the other day that I think will interest you.'

Her eyes laughing, Genieve insisted, 'Will you hurry up and tell me what this is about? I want to get back to the party.'

'I thought you might prefer Ross not to hear.'

'Hear what?' she said, puzzled. 'What wouldn't I want Ross to——?'

'Paul's coming back from New York,' Coralie cut in. 'Ostensibly he called to ask if I was interested in showing some of his work at the gallery, but what he really wanted to know was how you were and whether you were going with anyone.'

Genieve fingered the cord of her camera. Hearing Paul's name was no longer painful, but he had been a major force in her life for a long time. She couldn't pretend he'd never existed, never mattered to her.

'I know he's coming back from New York,' she said quietly. 'I heard from him a week ago.'

'You're being very cool about it,' her cousin observed a shade sharply. 'I thought he was the love of your life. For goodness' sake, this is your chance to marry him!'

'I don't want to marry him.'

'That's pride talking,' Coralie scoffed.

'No, it isn't. It's over between Paul and me. We weren't meant for each other, and if I hadn't been so infatuated with him I'd have realised it at the time.'

Her cousin considered her for an instant. 'I seem to have heard this speech before. The two of you were forever striking sparks off each other. I'll believe you mean what you say if you still haven't made it up with him when I get back from Hong Kong.'

Her certainty made Genieve impatient. 'It wasn't

some stupid little tiff we broke up over,' she reminded Coralie.

'If it's over, and you don't love Paul any more, then why are you getting angry?'

'Because. . .' she began, then broke off, seeing that Ross stood in the doorway, watching her, a hard enigmatic light in his eyes.

'Am I interrupting something?' he enquired mockingly, querying the sudden silence.

Coralie gave an embarrassed little laugh. 'It was just girls' talk, Ross. You know how I run on—I'm a real chatterbox once I get started.'

Touching him lightly on the arm, she went out. There was a suggestion of sympathy in the gesture. It annoyed Genieve, for it seemed to imply that she wasn't treating Ross fairly when in fact she'd done nothing wrong at all.

'So what's this about Paul?' he asked, and she sensed the anger behind his stern calm.

'He's coming back from the States next month, but it has nothing to do with. . .'

'Since I've asked you to be my wife, it has plenty to do with me,' he contradicted curtly.

'I was going to say it has nothing to do with *us*,' she said, flaring in spite of herself.

As before a storm, the atmosphere was charged, unpredictable, dangerous.

'In which case you won't object to giving me an answer to my proposal before September comes to an end,' he said sarcastically.

For an instant Genieve glared at him, angry and disbelieving.

'Are you issuing me with some kind of ultimatum?' she demanded.

'That's an odd turn of phrase,' he fired back. 'Or were you thinking that a little competition might spur Paul on to make a commitment to you this time?'

'For a man who claims to be in love with me, that's a damned hurtful remark!'

'I'm not Trevor,' he said gratingly. 'You might have been able to play him on a string, but it won't work with me.'

'I'm not playing you on a string!' she cried. 'And if that's what you think——'

He caught hold of her shoulders in a bruising grip as she made to whirl away from him.

'Let me guess,' he cut in, his mouth twisting.

'All right,' she flashed back, goaded into saying the words she had checked. 'If that's the opinion you have of me I don't know that I want to marry you!'

His eyes narrowed and he let go of her so abruptly she had to take a step backwards to keep her balance.

'Well,' he said harshly. 'Now we know.'

He stood, tall and uncompromising, his face set in wintry, forbidding lines, and just to look at him, to note the powerful grace in his stance, was to have a sharp inexplicable pain go through her.

'Yes, we do, don't we?' she hissed fiercely.

Pivoting swiftly, she went out into the hall. She returned to the party, making a pretence of joining in the conviviality. As she stood talking to some of her parents' friends her gaze clashed briefly with Ross's.

He was chatting to her mother, impressing her with his charm, she could see. A dark eyebrow lifted sardonically and she looked away, furious that, when their exchange of words had left her taut and inwardly trembling, he could look so calm, if a shade grim.

Evidently he was more adept at mastering his emotions than she was, or had it all been lies, his saying that he loved her? He'd certainly let her walk away from him very easily, she thought, simmering with feelings that were all the more intense for being repressed.

It wasn't until the party was over, the large rambling house utterly still and she was in bed, that her anger turned into wretchedness. She sat hugging her knees with her arms, her eyes smarting in the lonely darkness. She had preferred feeling angry. Anger didn't hurt so much.

Restlessly she got up and paced barefooted over to the window. Her white broderie anglaise nightgown fell in clean lines from the ribbon thin shoulder straps, while her hair cascaded like a river of silk down her back. There was something timeless about her loveliness as she gazed out into the night. The moon was shining brightly, silvering the gnarled apple trees in the orchard and patterning the lawn with dark eerie shadows.

She leant her forehead against the cold windowpane, her throat aching. Deep inside her was a tight pain that refused to be eased.

She didn't love Paul. Her argument with Ross had nothing to do with him; it was to do with her. She might have been able to let go of her mistrust of putting her happiness into someone else's hands if he hadn't rushed her.

But splitting up with Paul had hurt her badly, and instinct had told her that Ross could cause her just as much pain, if not more, if she didn't fight to keep her feelings for him in check. Slowly two tears brimmed her eyes and ran down her cheeks. She jerked her head up and wiped them away, angry with herself.

She had wanted to be in control of her own life. Well, now she was, she thought, fierceness masking the strong desire to cry. Ross had made no attempt to ask her to reconsider her hastily flung words and she had no intention of taking them back. They were both free now to go their own separate ways.

CHAPTER SIX

IT WAS well past midnight. Genieve sat on the bed, serene and still. Ross watched her curiously, a shaft of moonlight hitting his right shoulder, making the rounded muscles seem as though they had been carved from teak.

'Genieve?' He covered her hand gently with his own. 'Are you all right?'

His voice came to her as though from a great distance in the velvety darkness. Her lashes fluttered as she stared at him, trancelike.

The raven thickness of his hair was unusually ruffled, while his rugged features were thrown into sharp relief by the shadows. The masculine line of his uncompromising but sensual mouth drew her attention for a brief moment before her gaze travelled blankly to meet the look of quizzical concern in his astute dark eyes.

'I. . . I'm fine,' she murmured automatically, with no idea of what she was saying, or where she was.

She blinked as dimly she realised he was in bed. The white sheets that had slipped down around his hips emphasised the swarthiness of his hard lean body. She noted the gleaming strength in his broad chest, the tangle of dark hair. The scent of him was clean and male, and her heart seemed to jolt as the impact of his virility broke into her dream.

Still watching her, Ross made to slide out of bed, moving slowly as though afraid he might jolt her awake.

'Wait!' she insisted breathlessly. Clarity splintering through the misty waves of sleep, she clutched at his forearm. 'Wait a minute! This is *your* room!'

Ross smiled. 'Yes, this is my room,' he agreed with a trace of irony.

She let go of his arm. Gazing about her in bewilderment, she asked, 'What am I doing here?'

'You drifted in like a pale ghost a couple of minutes ago, sat down on the bed and spoke to me. I thought you were awake. I couldn't believe it when you weren't,' he said. 'It seems you've been sleepwalking. I was going to guide you back to your room when you woke up.'

'I. . . I haven't walked in my sleep since I was a child,' she said, still a little dazed.

'Something must have been on your mind, bothering you,' Ross answered. 'What was it, the erstwhile lover, or the row we had?'

As he spoke he let his masculine gaze drift over her, the blatant glint in his dark eyes making her suddenly shatteringly conscious of how revealing her nightgown was. Coupled with his words and his dry tone, it threw her on to the defensive.

'Neither,' she said, more emotion in the one clipped word than she would have wished. 'I'm sorry if I woke you.'

She would have risen, but he caught hold of her by the wrist. Slowly and very deliberately he drew her hand towards him, opening her fingers with his thumb before pressing his lips to her palm. In the silence of the night her sharply indrawn breath betrayed the response of her senses to his touch.

'Let me go! I'm going back to bed,' she said swiftly.

'Without getting what you came for?' queried Ross, a latent fierceness in the dark eyes that taunted her.

'I beg your pardon,' she retorted, anger trembling behind the frost in her voice, because with such an electric awareness between them she knew exactly what he meant.

'Don't you think it's significant that you chose my room to wander into?' he demanded, his face set hard.

It was significant, but, threatened by the force-field of sexual static, and becoming more sensitive and agitated by the minute, Genieve hit back with irony.

'The power of the subconscious mind, you mean?'

A black eyebrow arched sardonically at her, applauding the accuracy of her remark.

'That's precisely what I mean. Awake, you can keep your desires nicely bottled up. At night, it's a different matter.'

'Your conceit leaves me speechless!' she exclaimed in a voice that shook with fury. 'I've no idea why I wandered into your room, but it certainly wasn't because. . .'

She broke off, realising that temper had made her begin a sentence which now had her floundering. Rather than attempt to complete it, she surged to her feet and headed for the door.

But Ross had no intention of allowing her to dodge the issue. Throwing back the covers, he was out of bed and snatching up his robe in one tigerish movement. Shrugging it on, he came after her with the speed and silence of a hunter, spinning her round to face him as her hand touched the doorknob.

'Why not finish what you were saying?' he suggested with harsh mockery.

Her eyes sparkling, Genieve looked up at him, defiance in every slim line of her, although her heart was pounding. Beneath his robe he was obviously naked. She was aware of the muscles that rippled beneath the silk, aware of the glitter in his eyes.

The derision she saw in their depths changed her anger into a tight knot of resentment. There was more than a touch of the imperious in his stance and his features were infuriatingly controlled. Pain twisted her heart as she thought that, for all his avowal of love, she had none of the power over his emotions that he had claimed over hers in such a short time.

She took a step back, hissing through clenched teeth, 'Despite your arrogant assumption, I'm not so repressed I can't face up to the fact I'm. . .'

'Sexually attracted to me?' Ross cut in savagely. He pulled her to his chest, caressing her bare arms with hands that transmitted a message of banked-down anger and passion. Her blood began to tingle and, as though sensing it, he jibed, 'Bewildering, isn't it, still being tied to Paul, yet wanting to go to bed with me?'

'I'm not still tied to Paul!' she denied, whirling away from him, her voice dangerously unsteady. 'Not in any way. That was the conclusion *you* chose to jump to!'

Ross's eyes narrowed on her face. He stood stock still for an instant. The stern set of his mouth altered, softening his harsh expression.

'It's no wonder I can't get you fathomed,' he muttered, before commanding, 'Come here.'

'Why?' Her voice was a choked whisper, touchingly fierce.

He had never seen her quite so vulnerable. 'You

know damned well why,' he growled with husky tenderness.

He took a step towards her and, realising suddenly that he'd forgiven her for her wayward behaviour when she'd blazed that she wouldn't marry him, she went blindly into his embrace. Her fingers stole to his hard neck, the ache in her heart dispelled by a rush of relief so intense that tears dampened her lashes. Everything wasn't over after all!

Ross held her tightly, the roughness of his jaw grazing the softness of her cheek. She closed her eyes, savouring the iron feel of him, the arms that held her so possessively, the sweet, sweet poignancy of the moment.

'I'm sorry I flew off the handle with you this evening,' she whispered, her voice barely audible. 'When you said I had to give you an answer I. . . I started to feel pressured. I panicked.'

'Being in love frightens you, doesn't it?' he murmured.

Genieve nodded, searching for the words as she tried to explain.

'It's like living in some fragile paradise. Then, when it ends. . .'

Ross's warm hand left the slim curve of her back. Releasing her a little, he tilted her chin up.

'It's not going to end,' he told her with quiet intensity. 'Not for us.'

She didn't answer, but there was a hot glow in her tear-misted eyes, a look which said she believed him. Her lips felt dry and unthinkingly she touched them with the tip of her tongue.

His gaze followed the movement before travelling

over her, drinking in the soft swell of her breasts beneath the delicate nightgown, the lovely curve of her creamy shoulders. She caught her breath imperceptibly, the gentle mood changing as his scrutiny, and the dangerous intimacy of the night, charged the air with tension and desire.

'Ross. . .' She breathed his name in a sudden agony of need as he pulled her almost roughly against him.

And then everything faded from her vision except the hard, beautifully moulded mouth that swooped to claim her own. Her lips opened willingly under his as pleasure, fierce and pagan, licked along her veins. His kiss was like a pledge that began with melting gentleness and then deepened into thrusting passion.

When his hand cupped her breast she swayed, feeling so weak at the knees she thought she would fall. Ross's arm tightened around her waist, his stroking caress continuing as he kissed her. Trembling, she tangled her fingers into his dark hair, her body crying out for more of the hot, desperate excitement he claimed from her.

His lips found the throbbing pulse at the base of her throat and then, as he brushed aside the ribbon-thin straps of her nightdress, followed the path that his hands had laid bare. Her pale skin was flushed, the beautiful lines of her throat and breasts enhanced by the shadows.

'You're so lovely,' he muttered raggedly.

He laid his mouth against her breast, his hard lips becoming gentle as they closed over her nipple. His tongue brushed the aroused peak until she moaned, her fingers digging feverishly into the strong muscles of his back.

Aching for more of the hot frenzied pleasure he was

giving her, she clung to him, her heart thudding against his thirsty mouth. She heard him murmur her name, then felt him tense, a quiver of restraint running through the muscles of his strong, lean body.

She opened her eyes as he raised his head, confused to see that his expression was tight. Her pulses throbbing with the desire he'd kindled in her, she faltered huskily, 'Ross. . .?'

She blushed hotly as his glittering gaze ranged over her pale breasts. With hands that were gentle yet slightly unsteady, he slid the straps of her nightdress back on her shoulders. 'God, Genieve, you intoxicate me!' His voice was deep, throaty, sensual.

'Then kiss me,' she pleaded in a whisper, her arms going up around his neck. 'Kiss me again.'

But, before her slight form could brush against the hardness of his body, he swiftly caught hold of her hands, repulsing her embrace.

'Do you think I'm made of stone, woman?' he demanded, breathing hard, his mouth twisting wryly. 'If I kiss you again, one thing's going to lead to another.'

'Are. . .are you saying you want me to go back to my room?' she asked, a catch in her voice, unable to understand. She was ready to give herself to him, the intensity of her desire proof of her love. And now he was rejecting her, putting an end to what would have been an act of mystic union between them.

'No, damn it, that's not what I want!' he growled. 'What I want is to make love to you until this hungry longing inside me is satisfied. But when I take you for the first time, it's not going to be under your parents' roof after you've been sleepwalking.' He bent to kiss her mouth. Her lips were warm and yielding and she felt him hesitate an instant before he drew back. 'Believe me, there'll be a better time and a better place,' he said huskily.

She had wanted him so much. She still wanted him, but now that the wild tingling in her blood had subsided a little, she realised that he was right. Mastering the ache of disappointment inside her, she nodded mutely.

In the darkness that throbbed with feeling she reached up to touch his face fleetingly. Ross captured her hand, pressing his lips warmly, ardently into the hollow of her palm. Then she was at the door, the hem of her nightgown fluttering whitely as she slipped out on to the long landing.

Back in her room, her breathing still quickened, she sank down on the bed. Tentatively she brushed the tips of her fingers against her lips that throbbed faintly with the sensuous pressure of Ross's kiss. A tremor quivered through her. The fire he had lit had been so fervid that just to remember the way he had touched and caressed her was to have heat lick along her veins, to ache for him again in every nerve.

I love him, she finally acknowledged to herself, the admission accompanied by a kind of dazed elation, a trembling wonder that swept away all doubt. For all the giddy speed with which she had fallen in love with Ross, this was no illusion, no flowering of emotion that would wither with the first frost. This yearning, both conscious and subconscious, to bond with him, body, mind and soul, was forever.

The feeling of certainty was every bit as strong the next morning. Dressed in a pair of brown corduroy trousers, a scarf knotted at her throat, its ends falling attractively over her blouse, Genieve skipped downstairs.

Singing to herself, she went into the kitchen where her mother was seated at the breakfast table.

'Morning, Mother,' she began. 'What a lovely smell of bacon overlaid with toast and coffee! Am I the last one up?'

'Not by a long shot,' her mother smiled. 'Both your brothers are still in bed, and Clive's girlfriend hasn't put in an appearance yet.'

'I thought the house seemed very quiet.'

'Coralie was up early, though,' her mother remarked. 'She wanted to get on the road in good time to drive back to London. Now what would you like for breakfast?'

'Just toast and coffee,' Genieve answered. She sat down at the table and picked up the coffee-pot. Pouring herself a cup, she asked, 'Where's Ross?'

'Your father's taken the dogs for a run and Ross has gone along with him. He said he'd like to see a bit more of the village and have a look at the Severn. He seems very interested in everything—in you too, I think.'

There was a hint of enquiry in the comment. Still marvelling at the fervour with which she had fallen in love, Genieve said, her voice lending a telling eloquence to the simple statement, 'He's asked me to marry him.'

'And you're going to say yes,' her mother guessed after an instant's pause. Genieve nodded, her eyes shining. 'Oh, darling, I'm so happy for you!'

'I wasn't sure you'd understand,' Genieve laughed as her mother hugged her. 'It's all happened so quickly.'

'With another man I probably would be worried you

were rushing into something,' Mrs Dearing said. 'But with Ross, I can't explain it, but the moment I saw you together I felt that he was the man you were going to share your life with.'

'How did you know things were serious between us? I never said.'

'You didn't have to. I knew from the look in your eyes. Though I have to admit I was a bit puzzled as to what was going on. The atmosphere was so fraught between the two of you last night, I thought maybe you'd quarrelled.'

For a brief, terrible second Genieve thought of how nearly she had wrecked her chance of happiness by turning Ross down. Just to envisage the future without him was to feel cold. And then came the knowledge that Ross wouldn't have let things end between them even if she hadn't gone sleepwalking into his room.

Needing to tell him how much she loved him, she said impulsively, 'Which way did Ross and Dad go when they left the house?'

'They went down Merrywalk Lane,' her mother told her. 'I expect they'll come back across the fields and through the orchard to give the dogs a good run. If you set out now you should meet them in the far meadow.'

The distant ringing of the church bells carried in the crisp Sunday stillness as Genieve swung across the orchard where apples lay in abundance under the trees, half hidden in the long tufty grass. Wasps, drowsy with nectar, buzzed around them, drawn by the cidery fragrance, while spiders' webs were everywhere, outlined in silver by the heavy dew. The sun was shining, but there was the first nip of autumn in the air, a chill that made her glad she had stopped to put on a jumper.

She climbed over the stile with agile grace and jumped down, catching sight of her father and Ross almost the moment they came into view. But quick as she'd been to sight them, Ross was quicker still to spot her. He raised his hand in recognition and she waved back.

Striding over the rough ground, he looked tough and fit. Even from afar he gave the impression of strength and authority, a raw quality to his virility that drew her gaze like a magnet, before her attention was claimed by the two red setters that came racing across the meadow to her, barking a furious welcome.

She made a fuss of them and, having leapt up at her excitedly, they bounded off again.

'What do you think of the river?' she asked Ross as soon as he and her father came into calling distance.

'Very impressive,' he called back. He was wearing faded jeans that clung to his hips. His Burberry sweatshirt was short-sleeved and open at the neck to reveal the tanned column of his throat and the wiry hairs that matted his chest. It was obvious that he didn't feel the cold. Genieve would have been frozen in just a blouse.

'I think it takes a newcomer to make us realise how beautiful the Severn is,' her father joked as the three of them drew level. 'We locals take it too much for granted.'

Ross slid his hands in his pockets, the pull of his jeans enhancing his strong virile build.

'The river must be at least a mile wide where it sweeps round in that massive curve under the cliff,' he remarked.

'You want to see it when there's a big tide and a following wind,' Richard told him. 'A bore sweeps up,

a wall of water several feet high. It's quite amazing.'
He whistled to the dogs, adding affably, 'Well, I must
be getting back. Although it's Sunday I said I'd look in
at the Glebe Farm this morning. You two can take your
time.'

'OK, Dad.'

As her father headed in the direction of the house,
his red setters following him, Genieve's gaze returned
to Ross. The slanting sunlight accentuated his chiselled
features and dark good looks. There was a knowing
glint in his eyes and she found she was smiling, realising
suddenly that everything was certain between them
without her even uttering a word, such was the
emotional rapport between them.

'Well?' he prompted, teasing her with the timbre of
his deep flexible voice.

There was a bubble of joy inside her. She could never
remember being this happy ever before.

'Well, what?' she asked innocently, though her blue
eyes were dancing.

She gave a gasp as, in retribution for her cheek, Ross
lifted her off her feet and swung her round.

'Put me down!'

'Tell me,' he insisted, laughing with her.

'All right.' Breathless and laughing, she called a
truce. Her hand rested on his strong arms as he set her
down. Looking up at him, she said, her eyes aglow,
'It's only fair to warn you I'm not very good around the
house and I tend to burn things when I cook.'

'I take it that's an "I will",' Ross said, amused.

'Yes.' She nodded, and then, her voice husky as his
arms tightened about her swiftly and possessively, she
whispered, 'Oh, Ross, yes!'

His lips were warm and firm as he claimed her mouth in a long passionate dizzying kiss. She wound her arms tightly around his neck as she kissed him back, while all the time the joyous sound of the church bells carried across the fields.

When at last he raised his head they were both smiling.

'Do you want a big wedding, or shall we elope?'

Genieve knew he had no more intention of eloping than she had, but even so a shiver of excitement ran down her spine. Ross was strong and steady; he was also a man with enormous vitality and charm. Maybe that was why agreeing to be his wife seemed strangely akin to taking the decision to live dangerously.

'I don't mind what we do,' she whispered, her heart still hammering from his embrace. 'Just as long as we don't have to wait. Let's get married soon, Ross.'

Since most of their friends lived in London and her parents had no objections to the idea, they decided to hold the wedding in Harrow. Ross bought her a beautiful engagement ring, a showy emerald, flanked by two diamonds, and they chose the plain gold wedding ring at the same time.

But Genieve went alone to choose her wedding dress. She knew exactly what she wanted. It had to be romantic, ballerina-length with a fitted bodice and a full skirt. Her headdress was a whisper of veil held in place by a coronet of white gardenias. There were gardenias, too, in her bouquet, but she had freesias entwined with them to lend a glow of warm colour against the white.

Three weeks later at a simple civil ceremony Ross took her left hand, his eyes intent on her face, and slipped his wedding band on to her finger. She felt as if she was in a dream. She belonged to him now, the magical sense of completion they had discovered together would be theirs forever.

Her parents had reserved a suite for the reception at a hotel near Heathrow Airport. The food was excellent, the champagne flowed freely, and the touches of humour in the speeches added to the laughter and sense of fun. The best man read out the telegrams of congratulations, including one from Coralie, who was still on holiday in the Far East.

Later, having changed into a pretty blue suit with a silky blouse in printed crêpe de Chine, Genieve left with Ross to catch their flight to Milan. Amid a shower of confetti and good wishes she ducked into his Jaguar. He slid in alongside her, laughing as he brushed a mixture of lucky horseshoes and coloured bells from his thick dark hair.

They were driving along the busy airport perimeter road when he remarked with a smile, 'We're halfway there.'

'No, we're not. We've hardly begun our journey,' she laughed, teasing, 'You've drunk too much champagne, Ross.'

'You misunderstand me, my sweet.' His hand left the wheel to claim hers. 'I mean we're halfway to being man and wife.'

'Halfway?'

'We have a certificate, but the marriage hasn't yet been consummated.'

He was still smiling, but the look in his eyes changed as they flickered over her slim figure, making her blush. Ross was a very sensual man. Till now, knowing that she was a virgin, he had held the force of his desire in check, but tonight. . . Genieve's pulse quickened with the thought.

The flight was pleasant and uneventful, though there was slight turbulence as they crossed the Alps. After clearing Customs at Milan they picked up the Alfa Romeo in which they were to drive to the villa Ross owned on the shores of Lake Como. She hadn't known he had a house in Italy and she had been thrilled when he had suggested they spend their honeymoon there.

He drove fast and with easy skill, and soon the car was speeding away from the suburbs of Milan and along narrow twisting roads. Steep gradients gave views of pastel-washed houses and groves of lemon and orange trees.

The light was starting to fade when he said, 'I think we could do with a break. I'll pull in shortly. There's a good hotel a few miles on where we can have dinner.'

They didn't linger over the meal, as they had some distance to go yet. After leaving the hotel they went for a short stroll to stretch their legs and then returned to the car.

The soft Mediterranean night had closed in, the resting countryside, with its cypress trees and steeply shelving vineyards, barely visible in the darkness. They passed through the town of Como, which was full of bustle and activity, although it was late, and then drove parallel with the lake for some way. The lights of the houses sent silver ripples dancing over the satin-like surface of the water, while in the distance the mountains rose up shadowy and mysterious.

When at last the car turned off the road and into a gravel drive flanked by tall wrought-iron gates, Genieve was almost asleep. Ross gave her hand a squeeze.

'Wake up, wife. We're here.'

She gazed at the stately villa with its shutters and terraced gardens.

'Oh, Ross, it's beautiful!' she exclaimed, the ripple of delight that had gone through her with the word 'wife' intensified by the knowledge that the two of them had a whole fortnight to be alone together in these idyllic surroundings.

Ross's housekeeper, a plump middle-aged woman, dressed in black, was at the door to greet them, her face wreathed in smiles. She greeted Ross in Italian, her pleasure in meeting his bride obvious, though she could manage no more than a few words in English.

Her husband, who was the gardener, fetched the luggage from the car, while Ross led Genieve into the graceful drawing-room. The curtains were closed at the long windows. By day Genieve guessed that the views over the lake would be breathtaking.

Large, heavily gilded vases stood on marble-topped tables, some of them filled with flowers. Rich brocade cushions were scattered on the sofas, while a number of striking modern paintings graced the pale walls.

She moved from one to another and then stopped in surprise in front of 'Fantasy by Twilight'. It was an abstract picture, naïve yet sophisticated, and she had last seen it hanging in her cousin's elegant lounge. Now it hung next to another abstract by the same artist, making her realise that the two pictures had been painted as a pair.

'However did you persuade Coralie to sell "Fantasy by Twilight" to you?' she asked with a smile as Ross came to stand beside her.

'Your cousin's a keen businesswoman. I gave her a very good price,' he answered.

'You must have done,' she laughed, accepting the drink he handed to her.

He touched the rim of his glass lightly against hers as he said, 'To a long and happy future together.'

'To a long and happy future,' she returned softly.

'Preceded,' he said, 'by a long and happy night.'

His remark made her pulse leap with nervous excitement. Her gaze flew to his, the smouldering light she saw in his eyes sending a quiver of anticipation down her spine. Ross smiled. Gently he brushed her lips with his.

'Let's go upstairs,' he murmured.

Their bedroom was sumptuously furnished. French windows, hung with gold curtains, opened on to a balcony. Heavily brocaded chairs complemented the rosewood dressing-table and writing desk, while the bed had four slender posts at the corners.

While Ross showered, Genieve sat brushing her hair at the dressing-table, the lovely line of her shoulders enhanced by the cream silk and lace nightgown she was wearing. The lighting was dim and seductive. In the mirror she could see the large double bed behind her while her own reflection showed a woman ready for love. A tingle of pleasurable anticipation traced over her skin.

She was coming to Ross tonight for the first time. She remembered his stillness when she'd said she'd never been to bed with Paul. It had been the same morning that she had agreed to marry him. They had been walking back towards her parents' house, Ross's arm around her shoulders, and he stopped, tilting her chin up so that blushingly she was forced to meet his gaze.

'You mean I'm marrying an old-fashioned girl?' he had said, his searching tone tempered by a quizzical tenderness.

'I just wanted you to know I didn't sleep with Paul,' she had said huskily.

'Why didn't you, sweetheart?'

'Because I've always been a romantic,' she had whispered. Her colour had deepened as she said, 'I sort of wanted my virginity to be a gift for my husband on our wedding night.'

Ross smiled, a glitter of satisfaction in the depths of his eyes.

'Then that's what it will be,' he'd said, a sensual throb to his voice as he kissed her. 'Your gift to me.'

Her gaze flew to the mirror again as Ross came into the bedroom. He was wearing a robe of navy silk, and beneath it he was evidently naked. Her heart began to beat erratically as her eyes met his in the looking-glass.

'Not in bed yet?' he said softly.

'I was waiting for you,' she answered, then realised from the faint smile that played around his mouth that her words had an unintended meaning.

He spread out his hands.

'Here I am, so why not come to me?'

She stood up. As she did so, Ross's eyes, that were as dark as ink, travelled over her, taking in the quick rise and fall of her breasts beneath the filmy lace. His scrutiny sent a delicious tremor down her spine.

The room seemed to fade into a hazy backdrop so that only Ross, powerfully male, the muted lighting etching his chiselled features, was in focus. Genieve drank in the strong lines of his jaw and cheekbones, his sensuous mouth. Her heart fluttered as, obeying him, she crossed the distance between them.

'You're so beautiful,' he murmured as he drew her into his arms.

Her body was warm, but she was shivering with a mixture of excitement and a slight jittery fear of the unknown. As if to reassure her, Ross bent his head, brushing her lips with his. He explored the shape of her mouth very gently before pulling back a little to initiate another soft teasing kiss. A ripple of pleasure went through her and she began to respond, her mouth opening sweetly under his. As desire began to heat her body, timidity left her.

Ross's lips were against her temple. They moved, tracing the line of her face, heating her skin where he breathed. Her senses rushing, she kissed the craggy line of his jaw, wanting with a sudden desperate need to feel his lips on hers.

At last his mouth found hers again and, wild feverishness coursing through her, she clung to him, aware of every contour of his hard aroused body. His hands caressed her back, one palm travelling up her spine to slide beneath her fall of silken hair. Cradling the nape of her neck, he tilted her head back to plunder her mouth more deeply.

Her fingers tightened on his shoulders as a weak helpless pleasure went through her. She thought she was falling, then realised he had swept her off her feet and was carrying her towards the double bed. He laid her on the coverlet, his hand roaming over her body, loving and stroking until her senses were on fire.

'Ross. . .' she whispered breathlessly, wanting him never to stop kissing and touching her.

He slipped the ribbon-thin straps of her nightgown off her shoulders, sliding the delicate silk away from her as though he were unveiling a beautiful statue. Muttering husky endearments, he pressed his lips to her, tracing the path his eyes had taken with his thirsty mouth. As his lips found the hardness of her naked nipple she cried out his name, her fingers tightening in his hair. He was her love, the one man she wanted to give herself to completely and forever.

He shrugged his robe off and threw it aside, and she wound her arms around him, following as he led, the ecstasy building up inside her as his knowing fingers touched and stroked her. He allowed the pitch of pleasure to subside a little and then gathered it again until she moaned, the exquisite agony almost more than she could bear.

She arched against him, on fire for him to take her. And then, as he entered her, she gave a faint choked sob. She flinched a little with the pain of his first penetration, yet, consumed by the fierce flame of passion, she was aware of nothing save the blinding beauty of unity with him.

She clung to him, her fingers digging into his shoulders as his thrusting strength and male power sent her spinning out of control until suddenly the world seemed to explode in a starburst of light. Ross shuddered, his deep groan of fulfilment coming as, shaking and sobbing, she fell into dizzy freedom.

Afterwards they lay unmoving in the absolute peace that followed the storm. Ross drew her into his arms, holding her to him. His hand that stroked the slim plane of her back, caressing the indentations of her spine, conveyed a message of love and tenderness. She felt his chest rise and fall beneath her cheek as he gave a long, satisfied sigh.

'All right, sweetheart?' he asked softly.

'Blissfully all right.' She raised her head to look into his eyes. He was lying on his back, every line of his body relaxed and arrogantly indolent. Wonderingly she whispered, 'I never dreamed it would be so powerful, so overwhelmingly beautiful.'

He smiled, and, sweetly exhausted as she was by the pleasure he had given and taken, his sensual smile made her seem to stop breathing for an instant or two.

'We're very compatible, you and I,' he said, his lips capturing hers in a tender kiss. 'I'm glad it was good for you.'

Genieve nestled close to him. Her lips against his chest, she murmured drowsily, conscious of the care he had taken not to hurt her, the patience with which he had controlled the urgency of his own need so that they would reach the summit together, 'You made sure it was good for me.'

CHAPTER SEVEN

THE DAYS and nights of their honeymoon merged together in a golden haze. It was like some enchanted interlude stolen out of time, their desire for one another a source of permanent delight. They made love often. In the afternoons the sunlight would stream into their bedroom, bathing their naked bodies in its glow. At night there were the moon shadows and the sweet elusive fragrance of flowers that drifted in through the french window.

After the brightness and warmth of Italy, London seemed very drab as the plane made its descent through thick cloud. Genieve gazed out of the tiny window as the panorama of houses and roads appeared below. Second by second the perspective altered, the ground taking on a more familiar appearance as the plane came in to land. It was drizzling and in the rain the airport terminal looked grey and austere.

Sensing Ross's gaze, she turned her head.

'How does it feel to be home?' he asked, giving her a quick kiss.

She smiled at him. Her slight sadness was forgotten as she realised that, while their honeymoon was over, home now meant his house in Loudwater, and ahead of them lay all the excitement of starting their married life together.

'It feels good,' she told him, joking, 'in spite of the rain!'

Autumn had advanced in the fortnight they had been away. She saw, as they sped along the M25, that the horse-chestnuts were ragged, while the beech trees were a deep ochre. Escaped Michaelmas daisies blossomed in mauve clusters at the roadside.

They left the motorway at the Chorleywood turn-off and from there they were quickly at Loudwater. Ross's Tudor-style, architect-designed house was built overlooking the Chess valley. It was set well back from the quiet sloping road in wooded gardens.

Ross carried her over the threshold. Although she had spent a number of evenings at his house during their engagement, she glanced about her with pleasure, noting the bowl of roses and carnations that had been placed to welcome them on the hall table.

The door to the lounge stood ajar, giving a glimpse of the spacious and very masculine room that lay beyond. Ross's taste was for the modern, with an elegant touch here and there of the antique. The central heating was evidently on, for the whole house struck warm.

'I don't know about you, but I'd like a cup of tea,' Genieve announced.

'Good idea,' Ross answered. As he spoke he was leafing through his mail which had been left in a neat pile on the hall table.

'It may take me a minute,' she warned. 'I still don't know my way about in your kitchen.'

'Give me a shout if you can't find what you want,' he smiled. 'I'll bring the cases in from the car and take them upstairs.'

She carried a tray with the tea-cups and a plate of

petits fours into the lounge where Ross soon joined her.

'Shall we eat in or out this evening?' he asked.

'I'd like an evening at home,' she said.

'So we can have an early night?'

His voice was sensual. She felt her pulse quicken and wondered if there would always be this tense current of excitement charging the air. 'It's an idea,' she agreed, colouring a little.

The grooves on either side of his attractive mouth deepened as the flash of knowledge swept between them of the feverish rapture they would share later in bed. He set his cup down on the chrome and glass coffee-table.

'I'm going to have a quick shower and then make a few phone calls,' he said.

'And I'll see what I can rustle up for dinner.'

Genieve returned to the kitchen and opened the refrigerator, which was well stocked. She liked Ross's housekeeper, a pleasant efficient woman who came in on a daily basis, and was touched by Faith's thoughtfulness in seeing that everything for a quick meal was to hand.

There was a choice of fillet steak or lamb chops. She decided on the steak, prepared the vegetables, then went upstairs to ask Ross what time he wanted to eat.

She entered the master bedroom at the same time that he came out of the en suite bathroom, a towel wrapped low around his lean hips. The impact of his virility was so powerful it seemed to stop her breathing for an instant or two.

Magnificently male, when stripped he had the proud

bearing of an Apache warrior. His swarthy skin glistened with the last drops of his shower, and dampness darkened the black tangle of hairs of his naked chest. Genieve was always moved by the sight of his strong body, and her fascinated gaze travelled down the entire length of him before returning to his chiselled face.

'Do you have any idea what you do to me when you look at me like that?' he said, a growl of desire in his deep voice.

The awareness between them was so strong it was like a haze. Her lips felt suddenly dry and she moistened them as she said, her heart thudding with the joy of knowing that his need of her was as insatiable as hers was for him, 'I. . . I came to ask if you're hungry. Do you want to eat straight away?'

'I'm starving,' he murmured, his husky tone leaving her in no doubt as to what he meant.

He came towards her and she moaned softly as he pulled her possessively into his arms, feeling her senses rushing at the contact with his strong aroused body. He kissed her deeply, hungry for everything she could give him, and long before he laid her on the bed she was trembling, her ardent response adding heat to the flames of their passion.

Their lovemaking was wild and fierce, and as they joined together and gathered in pitch she cried out his name, gasping as the agony of pleasure became almost more than she could bear. She heard him groan and, as they reached the blinding summit together, she raked her nails helplessly down his back, exhausted and complete.

'Dinner may be a little late,' she teased some while afterwards when they were still naked in bed.

Ross pressed her back against the pillows, smoothing a strand of hair away from her face.

'Who cares?' he said roguishly.

They smiled at each other. She felt his strong brown fingers gently stroke the undercurve of her breast and as she gave a ragged sigh of pleasure she thought, it's all so perfect; together we're perfect.

During the next week she slipped into the new routine of married life as if she had been made for it. It was a busy and exciting time, especially so as, with Ross's encouragement, she had decided to expand the business. He understood that she was ambitious and, since her cottage in Harrow was on the market, he had suggested that when it sold she use the money to purchase a second shop. If she needed any extra backing, he said, he would provide it.

Sherry was delighted when Genieve asked her if she would be interested in taking over as the manager of the boutique in Northwood so that she could devote her attention to the new shop. Now all she was waiting for in order to go ahead was an offer on her cottage.

She spent Wednesday afternoon, which was early closing at the boutique, looking over two shops which had become vacant, then drove home. One had a particularly good location and, interested in it, she curled up on the sofa in the lounge to work out what the rates on it would be. She bit the end of her pencil thoughtfully and then glanced up, hearing the doorbell.

'Coralie!' she exclaimed as she opened the front door wide. 'How lovely to see you! I've been meaning to get in touch. Come on in.'

'Well, you've certainly landed on your feet,' her

cousin observed, looking up at the house before stepping into the hall. 'How are you enjoying being mistress of the manor?'

'I'd be happy with Ross anywhere, even in a garret,' Genieve laughed. 'Here, let me take your coat.'

Her cousin was smartly dressed as always. Beneath her long camel coat she wore lean beige gabardine trousers and a lambswool polo-neck, casual but chic. Her hair was loose, the windblown style framing her face attractively.

Genieve led the way into the kitchen and plugged in the percolator.

'How was Hong Kong?' she asked chattily.

'Hong Kong was fine.' The slight shrug that accompanied the answer said the topic wasn't worth discussing.

'I'm sorry you were away for my wedding. Would you like to see the photographs?'

'All beautifully bound in a white leather album threaded with white satin ribbon, no doubt,' her cousin remarked. There was a sarcastic note in her voice, and Genieve gave her a quizzical glance. Coralie smiled as though she'd only been teasing. 'You know,' she said, 'when I got your telegram saying you were getting married, I thought you meant you were marrying Paul.'

'But I told you. . .'

'Yes, you did, didn't you?' Coralie interrupted. 'I should have listened.'

They sat in the lounge to drink their coffee. With a fire burning in the modern grate it was a comfortable room, the Persian carpet adding a richness to the décor.

Genieve shook her head as her cousin leaned forward to offer her a cigarette.

'No, thanks,' she said. 'Ross doesn't like me smoking, so I'm trying to give up.'

'If you do you'll put on weight. Everyone always does.'

'Don't dishearten me!' Genieve protested with a laugh. She went on, 'I was going to phone you to say we're having a dinner party on Sunday. I hope you can come.'

Her cousin inhaled smoke, lifted her chin, and blew it out while saying, 'A dinner party. How nice.'

'To be honest, I'm a bit nervous about it,' Genieve admitted with a smile. 'It will be the first time I've entertained as Ross's wife.' Something unreadable flickered in the green eyes that regarded her and she prompted, 'Can you come?'

Instead of answering, her cousin stood up and paced towards the fireplace. Her shoulders quivered with laughter before she turned back to face Genieve, poised, cool and mocking.

'You'll have to forgive me if I seem a shade bemused,' she said, 'but this whole situation is so bizarre.'

'Bizarre?' questioned Genieve, confused by her cousin's attitude.

'I keep thinking I should be the one giving the dinner party on Sunday and you should be the guest in this house.'

'I don't follow you.'

'No, I don't suppose you do,' her cousin sneered. 'I'm sure Ross had far more tact than to tell you that before he asked you to marry him, he asked me.' There was an ashtray on the mantelpiece. Coralie tapped her cigarette against it as she added pointedly, her lips curving in a cold smile, 'Geoff, the bastard, refused to give me a divorce.'

Genieve stared at her, emotion bringing a rush of colour into her face that died as quickly as it had come. She was on her feet, refusing to think how Geoff had been at the nightclub that evening, how everything fitted.

'I don't believe you!' she cried, her voice shaking a little.

Her cousin smiled again. 'You don't really think you were Ross's first choice, do you?' Her eyes glittered with triumph and malice as she stated, 'The two of us were lovers before he even met you. Ross married you purely because he needs a wife, someone to entertain for him and to be a social asset.'

Genieve's heart was beating unevenly.

'I don't believe you!' she repeated, desperately trying to hide the surge of doubt. 'I love Ross and he loves me.'

'You think so?' her cousin returned derisively. She picked up her clutch bag that lay on the coffee-table and tucked it under her arm. 'Let me give you some advice, little cousin. Ross is rich, powerful and fantastic in bed. Be satisfied with what you've got while it lasts.'

'What do you mean, while it lasts?'

'I would have thought it was obvious. When Ross realises it's never going to be as good between the two of you as it was between him and me, he'll divorce you.'

'I won't listen to another word!' Genieve said fiercely. 'I won't let you spoil everything with your lies!'

Her cousin strolled to the door. Pausing there on her

way out, she said with spite, 'Lies? Why not ask Ross about it?'

The sultry perfume she wore lingered in the air even after she had gone. Genieve sank down in the nearest armchair. Her knees felt shaky and her temples were throbbing. She didn't want to believe what her cousin had said, but her peace of mind was shattered.

Would Ross have married her cousin had she been free? 'No,' she whispered aloud, clenching her nails into her palms, 'I won't think it!' Yet why should her cousin be lying? Had she been Ross's mistress? Was that why the painting 'Fantasy at Twilight' hung in his villa, her cousin's decision to part with the favourite picture proof of her love?

'Stop it! an inner voice demanded, but Coralie had sown the seed of uncertainty in her mind and she could not stop. She had been trusting once before, only to find that her trust had been misplaced. Paul's betrayal had scarred her deeply, making it impossible for her to shut out the dark clamour of suspicion.

A log fell in the grate, sending up a shower of sparks, but, tormented by doubt and jealousy, Genieve didn't hear it. Nor was she aware of the twilight that steadily invaded the room. A sense of impending calamity made her heart thump. Her love for Ross was the cornerstone of her life. It would destroy her if what her cousin had said was true, that he had married her solely as a social asset. And if he ever left her. . .

Pain slashed at her heart, followed by a blaze of anger as she pushed the idea away. He wasn't going to leave her. Theirs was a strong marriage. She thought of the desire that smouldered in his eyes when he kissed her, the possessive way he drew her into his arms, all the sweet nights of passion they had shared. Ross loved her. She knew he loved her!

She drew a deep breath, determined to get a grip on herself, to stop being so irrational. And then Coralie's parting words flashed cruelly into her memory. 'Why not ask Ross about it?' Because I don't dare, came the answer, a terrible uncertainty taking hold of her again.

What if Ross should tell her that he and Coralie had been lovers? It still doesn't mean he asked her to marry him, she thought fiercely. But suppose he had. . . She didn't think she could bear it if Ross should confirm what her cousin had said.

It was better not to ask, not to know. And yet she had to know. Feeling cold, she stretched out her hand towards the fire. But it wasn't the fire's warmth she needed, it was reassurance from Ross, reassurance she hadn't the courage to seek lest it wasn't forthcoming.

The doorbell rang, breaking into her thoughts and making her realise how long she had sat in the gloom, staring into the fire, but she didn't go to answer it. She felt she couldn't face anyone right now. She was too upset, too shaken.

She pressed her knuckles against her trembling lips, glad that the bell didn't ring again. Whoever the caller was, he had obviously assumed that no one was home.

She stood up with the intention of switching on the lamp and drawing the curtains—then gave a terrified gasp as she saw that a man stood silhouetted in the doorway.

'Genieve. . .?'

Her panic abated as she recognised the voice.

'Paul!' she breathed shakily. 'What are you doing here? How did you get in?'

His hand went to the light-switch that was beside the door. The sudden brightness made her pupils dilate so that her eyes looked even darker in her white face.

'The front door was ajar,' he explained. 'When I rang and got no answer I wondered if everything was all right.' His gaze narrowing on her, he added, 'I can see that it's not.'

'Everything's fine,' she insisted, her voice husky. 'You. . .you gave me a fright, that's all. Coralie was here earlier. She couldn't have shut the front door properly when she left. When I saw you I thought you were an attacker who'd broken in.'

'It's no wonder you look as if you need a drink,' he answered.

The house might have been his own, the way he crossed over to the drinks cabinet and poured two large brandies. Six months ago Genieve's heart would have leapt at the sight of his tall figure. Now she felt nothing except an intense wish that he hadn't called.

'Here, this should make you feel better,' he said, handing her a glass before sitting down on the sofa.

'Are. . .are you back in England for good?' she asked. She didn't know what to say to him, or why he had come. 'You didn't answer my letter saying I was getting married.'

The only reason she had written to him was that she thought he might be returning from New York purely to see her. She had wanted to make it clear that it was over between them, to save him a wasted trip.

'There didn't seem much point in answering it,' Paul said, a wry twist to his mouth.

There was a short silence. If only Ross would come home, she thought. She wanted to be close in his arms, to believe as he kissed her that he loved her as much as she loved him, that her cousin's claims were false.

After she and Paul had carried on an awkward and stilted conversation for some minutes she observed, glancing at the clock, 'I hadn't realised it was so late.' She hoped Paul would take the hint, finish his drink and go. 'Ross gets in at seven and we usually eat then.'

Paul looked at her, a brooding expression in his grey eyes. He ran his hand through his tobacco-brown hair, an angry gesture she knew of old.

'God, I was a fool to let you go!' he muttered.

'Paul, don't,' she said quickly.

'Why the hell did you do it?'

'Do what?' she said, beginning to snap because her nerves were stretched taut and, on top of everything else, she couldn't cope with his temper.

'You knew I loved you,' he said, coming over to where she sat. He knelt beside her, snatching up her hand and laying her palm against his cheek. 'You had no right to marry someone else when I still wanted you.'

Genieve withdrew her hand and, pushing him away, got swiftly to her feet. Paul's fierce intensity and brooding charm no longer moved her.

'I think you'd better go,' she said, her voice firm and calm.

'You're heartless!' he exclaimed bitterly.

'*Me*, heartless!'

'Do you think I meant to hurt you?' he demanded. 'I just didn't want to be tied down. I was too dependent on you, on what we had. The only reason I started sleeping with Vanessa was to break the hold you've always had on me. But I still love you.'

'I don't want your love,' she said, then turned away, pain squeezing her heart. It was Ross's love she wanted. Her eyes began to sting as she realised suddenly how cruel her words had been. If Paul felt as wretched as she did at this moment. . . She turned back and said more gently, 'You mustn't say these things. It's no use. Can't you see it's over between us?'

'Is it? When I came to see you I promised myself that it would be the last time, that I'd wish you well, then say goodbye. I didn't know then that I'd find you close to tears. . .'

'I'm all right,' she cut across him. 'Please, Paul, please go.'

Grey eyes pinned her, then he stated, 'It isn't working with Ross, is it?'

'Of course it's working!' she answered with all the more passion because she was so hurt and so unsure.

'Does he love you?' Paul demanded.

Genieve wanted to say yes, but her throat was choked and the word just wouldn't come.

'So that's it!' he said. 'That's why, far from being the radiant bride, you look so wan.'

'Stop jumping to conclusions!' she cried. 'I'm happy with Ross, happier than I ever was with you!'

Paul's jaw tightened. He reached inside his jacket and took out a card and pen.

'This is my phone number,' he said, writing it down. 'It's easy to remember, three sevens in the number. Call me when you decide to face up to the fact that you were never meant for anyone but me.'

'You don't seem to understand. I love my husband!'

'You married him on the rebound,' Paul said fiercely,

coming towards her and taking hold of her by the shoulders. 'What we had isn't dead. Admit it!'

Her eyes sparking, she tried to break his grip, but he pulled her tightly against him. She pushed at his upper arms, turning her head aside in a desperate attempt to evade his kiss.

'No!' she snapped, the rest of her furious protest stifled as his suffocating mouth came down on hers.

'Take your hands off my wife!' Ross's savage voice slashed into the room.

Genieve staggered as Paul let her go as though he had taken hold of a red-hot object. She felt sick and was trembling. Her heart plummeted with dismay as she saw the expression on Ross's face. She could imagine how the scene must have looked from the doorway and, just as when she'd been a child she'd coloured when she'd been accused of something she hadn't done, she blushed now in the same way.

Ross didn't move from where he stood, yet even his stillness seemed a threat. A nerve jumped in his lean jaw and his eyes held a murderous glitter as they remained fixed on Paul

'Get out of here,' he ordered grimly.

Paul's hand stole nervously to his collar. In height the two men were equal, but he had none of the honed power that was stamped in Ross's hard physique, nor did he have his mettle.

Yet he found the temerity to say, 'I was the one Genieve should have married, but don't worry—I'm leaving.'

The goading reply was ill-advised. Ross waited till he went to pass him, then his hand shot out. Slamming

Paul against the door-frame, he warned, 'Set foot in this house again and I'll smash you to a pulp!'

'Ross, stop it!' Genieve broke in jerkily, her skin prickling with alarm.

His gaze swung to her before returning to Paul. Cringing away from her husband's bone-breaking grip, his shoulders were hunched up around his ears. Ross's lips curled derisively. He stepped back, allowing Paul to go free, like a gladiator sparing an opponent too miserable to fight.

Paul hurried into the hall, his attempt not to look cowed a total failure. The front door banged seconds later.

In the throbbing silence that followed Ross studied Genieve with hard eyes that held a chilly glint. The anger and contempt she saw smouldering beneath the ice set her heart beatng unevenly.

'It's not what you think,' she began at once.

'You don't know what I think,' he bit back, the clipped derision in his voice an indication of how tightly he held his temper in check. 'Not yet!'

'Yes, I do. It was written all over your face when you came in and saw. . .'

'You and your ex-lover in that ardent clinch?' he cut in caustically. 'Evidently I came home earlier than you expected.'

His sarcasm was like a knife-thrust. Suddenly she was angry too, angry and hurt. How dared Ross condemn her so swiftly for something she hadn't done when, if her cousin was telling the truth, he was the one who dealt in deceit?

'Just what are you accusing me of?' she burst out. 'I

know how it must have looked when you walked in, but I can explain.'

'Why don't you?' he suggested gratingly.

There was nothing in his sardonic tone to suggest he loved her, and his eyes, that were like chips of flint, held only an implacable coldness. He was angry solely because her supposed unfaithfulness was a blow to his male pride, she thought wildly.

'What's the use?' she cried bitterly. She made to turn away, but he caught hold of her. 'Let go of me! You're not interested in what really happened, only in confirming your suspicions!'

'Don't come the angry innocent with me,' he rasped. 'Are you going to tell me you *didn't* invite Paul round, you *didn't* offer him a drink? He *wasn't* kissing you!'

'That's right, *he* was kissing *me*!' she sparked. 'I couldn't stop him. And I didn't invite him round, or let him in. The front door was open. . .'

'What kind of fool do you take me for?' Ross exploded, gripping her by the shoulders.

'I don't have to apologise for something I haven't done!' she declared, scarcely aware that his strong fingers were bruising her.

The ring of defiance in her voice carried conviction. Ross relaxed his grip on her. His jaw was still tight, his self-control as formidable as his fury had been as he said, his voice cold and toneless, 'Don't *ever* let me come in to find you with your ex-lover again. If you do I'm liable to break every bone in your nubile little body.'

'Was that why you married me, for my nubile little body?' she flung at him, her eyes blazing while hurt wrenched at her heart. 'You knew I'd been involved with someone else when I married you. At least I was honest about it!'

'Meaning?' he snapped.

'Meaning. . .' She broke off, her heart thumping painfully. When Ross had walked in to find her engulfed in Paul's embrace she had not been half as frightened as suddenly she was now. She clenched her fingers into her palms as she said haltingly, 'Were you and my cousin lovers?'

'No,' he answered, but he said it just a split second too late for it to ring true.

Tears stung her eyes.

'Who told you we were lovers?' he demanded harshly.

'What does it matter who told me?' she cried. 'What matters is that it's true, that you're lying to me!'

He swore under his breath.

'I've never lied to you,' he stated, controlling his anger.

He reached for her, but she shied away.

'Not when you said you loved me?' she countered fiercely. 'Not when you said you and Coralie were friends, nothing more?'

'Genieve, listen!'

He caught hold of her arm, but she retreated from him as though she couldn't bear to have him touch her.

'Listen to what?' she hissed. 'More lies?'

She pivoted, but he spun her back to face him. He looked as if he was sorely tempted to shake her, but, making a Herculean attempt to stop the rift between them widening irreparably, he began, 'For God's sake. . .' He halted mid-sentence as he noticed Paul's card that was lying on the coffee table. Picking it up, he said in an ominously quiet voice, 'What's this?'

'It's Paul's phone number. He. . .'

'So you can arrange another clandestine meeting with him?'

Genieve had no intention of seeing Paul again, but, wanting to hurt Ross in retaliation for the way he had hurt her, she said as he ripped the card in two and flung it savagely into the fire, 'Do you think that's going to stop me meeting Paul if I want to? I should have married him. I wish I had married him!'

She saw his expression harden and felt a fierce, malevolent satisfaction that she had succeeded in striking back. He came towards her, anger lending a pagan grace to his strides. With his gaze sliding over her, he pulled her against his chest. There was contempt and bitterness in his eyes, together with a glitter of fury and desire.

'You may still be in love with Paul, but you happen to be my wife,' he said harshly. 'Maybe it's time I reminded you of that.'

Combing his hands into her burnished hair, he tipped her head back, kissing her angrily, uncaring if he hurt her. She tried to hit out at him, but her hands were quickly caught and held.

She made a muffled sound of protest deep in her throat, and as she did so Ross drew her into a yet more intimate fit with his powerful male body. His lips were implacable, hard and sensuous as they forced hers to part for him. Then he was plundering her mouth, holding her so tightly she could feel the size and strength of him in every inch of her.

To her shame and dismay an arrow of need went

through her. She stopped fighting him. Before she could resist the madness, her hands were sliding around his neck as a whirlpool of desire, dizzy and intense, had her mind reeling.

She felt the softness of the cushions against her back and realised that he had lowered her on to the sofa. Arching her to him, he began to unbutton her blouse with deft, sure fingers. She threw back her head with a shock of pleasure as he caressed her, the angry passion she sensed in him awakening something equally untamed and elemental in herself.

And then she remembered Coralie. The fire that heated her blood was suddenly doused, jealousy and fury swamping her. This wasn't love. It was her cousin Ross loved.

In a tumult of angry despair she began to struggle. Ross raised his head, a black scowl on his face as he used his strength to hold her like some prisoner before bending to kiss her again.

She tried to turn her head aside, but he took hold of her chin. She could feel his hard arousal and, horrified by their sexual grappling, she sobbed, 'Let go of me! I hate you!'

'Hate? Is it hate when you make those gasping little moans, when you arch against me?' he muttered.

He cupped her breast in his hand and put his mouth to it. A shudder went through her, the pleasure her body found in his touch a torment to her mind. Ross laughed softly at her response and she struck out at him, a cry escaping her as his strong hands clamped on her wrists.

'Do you respond to Paul the way you respond to me?' he demanded harshly.

'At least he never tried to rape me!'

The ugly word made a tremor go through the hands that gripped her. She felt Ross tense. His jaw tightened.

'No, and he never asked you to marry him either, did he?' he said savagely as he released her.

Sobs threatening to choke her, Genieve drew her blouse around her as Ross strode from the room, his face dark, the frustration of a jungle panther caged in every line of him.

CHAPTER EIGHT

ALONE, Genieve sat with her face buried in her hands, fighting the tears that welled up inside her. But it was a long time before she had them checked and could raise her head.

She thought of Ross and her cousin together and curled her nails into her palms against the sharp uprise of anguish. And then, as she wondered if he had thought of Coralie every time he'd made love to her, she wanted to seize the nearest ornament and hurl it against the fireplace in a tempest of grief and anger.

Why, why had she let herself love him? How could she have been such a fool as to place her happiness in a man's hands? Had she learned nothing from her relationship with Paul? Twice now she had let her heart rule her head and twice she had been betrayed. Marry in haste, repent at leisure, she thought bitterly. How very true the saying was!

Ross had proposed to her because the woman he wanted had a husband who wasn't prepared to let her go and because in order to entertain he needed a wife. She was nothing more than a substitute.

It wasn't to be endured! She sprang to her feet. She had no intention of continuing to live in the same house with a man who didn't love her. She got as far as the door into the hall before her heart started to pound. Without Ross there would always be this ache of incompleteness tearing her apart.

Surely the pain of staying was better than the agony she would suffer if she walked out? If Ross had really loved her cousin, wouldn't he have waited the five years for her to be free? The thought lent her courage. Instead of waiting, he had chosen to marry Genieve. It had been a calculated decision, but perhaps in time he would come to love her.

Except that time wasn't on her side. It was on her cousin's. Coralie would get her divorce, and then what would happen to her marriage?

'Oh, God!' she whispered shakily, in dread of the future.

Her next thought steadied her. Ross had said once that he believed in commitment. He wouldn't have married her if he'd had doubts about their marriage lasting, she told herself. She remembered all the passionate moments they had shared. They had to mean something—they had to!

The trouble was that, while she loved Ross desperately enough to swallow her pride, to stay and work at her marriage against all the odds, anger kept intervening. Perhaps if she'd been less fiery she could have accepted that she was second best. But was it in her nature to wait patiently in the hope that maybe some day he would discover that he truly loved her, that she was first in his heart after all?

She paced restlessly about the room, finally perching on the edge of an armchair and staring miserably into the fire. Was it really only a few hours ago that she had been curled up on the sofa planning her next business venture and looking forward to a quiet, intimate evening with Ross when he came home?

When she had pulled herself together she went into

the hall. She had two choices: to accept her marriage as it was, or to walk out because she couldn't accept that it wasn't as perfect as it had seemed. Either from realism or love she had decided on the former.

She went into the kitchen—then stopped as she saw Ross. He had changed out of his business suit and was wearing jeans and a pullover which made her very conscious of the breadth of his chest. His hair gleamed blackly in the overhead lighting.

'I didn't think you'd feel like cooking this evening,' he began evenly.

'I don't,' she agreed, her tone cool, 'but I'll prepare dinner anyway.'

'You don't have to. It's already in hand. I'll have it ready in about twenty minutes.'

Feeling out of place in the kitchen when there was nothing for her to do, Genieve went into the dining-room and automatically began to lay the table. The candlesticks she left where they were on the sideboard. The romance in her relationship with Ross had shattered into a myriad pieces. It would take more than the soft play of candlelight to rekindle it.

They ate the meal in chilly silence. The lasagne Ross had cooked was delicious, but the atmosphere was dense with recriminations, and Genieve had to force her food down.

She made the coffee, aware of Ross's gaze on her as she poured it out. Briefly she raised her eyes to his, passing his cup to him. The tension in the air flared and her hand began to shake so that the cup rattled in its saucer.

With a mirthless smile Ross took it from her.

'Why so on edge?' he asked.

'You know damned well why I'm on edge!' she sparked.

'Because of Paul?' he jeered softly.

'No, not because of Paul, because. . .'

She broke off, and he ordered curtly, 'Go on.'

She shook her head. She felt too drained and too hurt to want to discuss their marriage. 'I'd rather we changed the subject,' she said.

'I was hoping,' he replied sarcastically, 'you might be able to come up with some kind of explanation as to what was going on here when I came home this evening.'

'I tried to give you an explanation. You weren't prepared to listen!'

'I'm prepared to listen now.'

But he didn't sound as though he were. He sounded hard and impossible to convince.

'I think I'm the one who's owed the explanation,' she said bitterly.

'Playing for time?'

The savage edge to his mockery made Genieve instinctively check her angry retort. Her face tight and closed, she sipped her coffee, trying to ignore the simmering tension between them, and aware that he was watching her with dark hawkish eyes.

'You haven't drunk your coffee,' she observed when she set her cup down.

'No,' he agreed.

He was still studying her and, unnerved by his scrutiny, she fingered the handle of her cup. Her teaspoon tinkled as she placed it on the other side of her saucer. It frightened her how furious she felt beneath the façade of brittle coldness.

She stood up to clear away the moment Ross had drained his cup, thankful that the ordeal of dinner was over and that she could escape to the kitchen, where she slowly stacked the dishwasher.

It was late and, when she had finished, she debated whether to go upstairs, or whether to join Ross in the lounge. After the row that had exploded, how were they ever going to put things right? she wondered wretchedly. And yet if she wasn't prepared to make some effort she might as well pack her things now.

The television was on and Ross was at the drinks cabinet fixing himself a whisky when she walked in. If he was surprised that she had decided to join him he didn't show it.

'Would you like a nightcap?' he asked.

'I'll have a liqueur.'

He poured her a Tia Maria. Her nerves tensed a little as he approached, and she kept her gaze on the television as though absorbed in the programme that had just started.

'Do you want to watch any more?' he asked when, after ten mintues of the sit-com, neither of them had managed to raise a laugh.

'No,' she said. Drinking the last of her liqueur, she went on, 'I'm tired. I think I'll go to bed.'

There was a hint of cynicism in the twist of his mouth.

'In the guest-room?' he ventured.

Genieve hadn't decided until that moment to move out of their bedroom, but his derision made her retort, her temper getting the better of her, 'Yes, in the guest-room. Or do you have any objections?'

'I have plenty of objections, but I'm not going to force myself on you,' he said sarcastically.

'That's nice to know,' she snapped.

As she headed for the door, he asked over the rim of his glass, his tone derisively polite, 'Perhaps before you go you'll tell me something. Why did you join me for a drink, since it obviously wasn't so we could talk?'

'What exactly is there to say?'

Her bitter question remained unanswered as she left the room.

The rift between them was one which remained unhealed. Genieve was glad that the business kept her so fully occupied. At least at the boutique she could forget for a while the pressure her marriage was under. There was no repetition of their furious row, but when the weekend came she and Ross were still sleeping apart and the atmosphere in the house was taut.

It was Sunday and she was laying the table for the dinner party they were giving when the phone rang. She glanced up, then, hearing Ross's step in the hall, realised he intended answering it, and carried on with what she was doing.

When he came in she was at the sideboard. In an impeccably tailored grey suit, white shirt and diamond-patterned tie he looked urbane and virile.

'That was Coralie to say she and Geoff will be late,' he told her.

'Coralie?' she exclaimed in surprise, staggered by her cousin's nerve. It had never struck her that Coralie would come to her dinner party after what had passed between them. Her mouth tightened as she turned back to the table that would now need two more places set.

Ross's keen gaze narrowed on her.

'You *were* expecting your cousin, weren't you?' he probed.

'No, as a matter of fact, I wasn't,' she said tartly, 'not after what happened when she called round.'

'When was this?' he asked. She didn't answer, and he took hold of her arm, forcing her to face him. 'I said, when was this?'

'She called round on Wednesday afternoon.'

'So *she* was the one who spun you that yarn that the two of us were lovers,' he said, the pieces falling into place.

'It was a yarn, was it?' said Genieve with cold irony.

'Will you stop playing the wronged wife for an instant and listen to what I have to say?'

Her eyes hostile, she said, 'I don't want to know about you and my cousin. Now will you please let me get on with laying the table?'

'Damn the dinner party! You and I are going to talk.'

His grip on her arm tightened as he propelled her into the lounge.

'You're hurting me!' she protested. Pulling away from him, she rubbed her arm resentfully.

'Be thankful I don't shake you senseless!' he snapped.

'And you be thankful I don't walk out on you!' she flashed back.

'Over what?' he demanded. 'Some trumped-up tale your cousin invented?'

'It sounded very convincing to me.'

'Sit down,' he ordered.

The snap in his voice made her obey him, but her eyes remained mutinous, and the set of her mouth was stubborn.

Ross stayed where he was, standing. He seemed taller than ever towering over her, his black brows drawn together in a frown. Striving for patience, he took a deep breath and began,

'I realise I should have said this the other night. Because I didn't, it's going to be harder now to convince you that what I'm telling you is the truth. But I'd come home to find you with Paul and I was feeling pretty murderous. I wasn't in any mood to launch into an account of something that happened three years ago.'

'Three years ago?' Genieve queried sceptically, jealousy clawing at her. 'That wasn't Coralie's story.'

'No, I don't imagine it was. She has a flair for the dramatic. If I know her, she'd manage to make it sound much more than it was.'

'She said you were lovers,' Genieve repeated the accusation.

'Well, we weren't. I met Coralie at an exhibition in Milan. As you know, she's very scintillating, very sharp, very witty. I was. . .'

'Bowled over?' she supplied in a brittle voice.

'No, I wasn't bowled over. I was. . .fascinated, I suppose is the word. But our affair, if that's what you want to term it, was over almost before it had begun. I picked her up at her hotel one evening, and as we were leaving a phone call came through from Geoff. I'd no idea until then that she was married. She was as angry about my learning that she had a husband as I was. And that's all there is to tell.'

'All? Do you expect me to believe that when I met you at her party?'

Exasperation glittered for a moment in Ross's eyes. He sat down beside her and she turned to look at him, the tilt of her chin defiant as she tried to hide how vulnerable she felt.

'I ran into your cousin in London a few weeks ago,' he explained. 'She knew I collected paintings and she also knew I wanted to buy "Fantasy at Twilight". She told me she was having a party and suggested I drop in some time during the course of the evening so we could negotiate a price.'

There was a short silence, then Genieve said in a hushed voice, 'She said you'd asked her to marry you and that when Geoff wouldn't give her a divorce you married me as second best.'

'And since she's your cousin you believed her.' Ross's tone was dry.

His dark hawkish gaze held an impatient glint and, filled with a strange mixture of irritation and relief, she demanded, 'Why didn't you tell me this on Wednesday? Why did you let me go through four days of hell believing——?'

'You seem to have forgotten this all flared up on the evening I came home to find you in Paul's arms,' he interrupted.

'I didn't want him to kiss me,' she declared. 'If you hadn't been so furious I'd have been thankful you walked in when you did. From the moment Paul arrived all I wanted was for him to leave.'

The hardness went out of Ross's face. Quietly, almost on a note of humour, he said, 'Have we both been fools, you and I?'

'Yes!' she said, a glow in her eyes. 'Why didn't you trust me?'

He pulled her close. 'I was afraid that what Paul said might be true, that what was between you wasn't dead.

When I met you at your cousin's party you *were* on the rebound from him,' he reminded her.

'I didn't marry you on the rebound,' she whispered, her arms going up around his neck, the last of her sentence all but lost as his mouth came down demandingly on hers.

She threaded her fingers into the raven thickness of his hair, her lips parting sweetly as she kissed him back, her response all the more ardent and complete because of the cold aching nights she had spent without him. His mouth was hungry yet tender. Shivers of joy danced over her skin as his hands caressed her.

'Tell me you love me,' he commanded when at last, reluctantly, he raised his head.

Genieve looked up at him, her lips throbbing from their long insatiable kiss. His eyes that smiled at her were dark and brilliant, and she whispered teasingly, 'Do you honestly need to hear me say it?'

'Perhaps I'll let you show me instead.'

He found her mouth again, and as she melted against him, surrendering utterly to the invasion of his kiss, he groaned deep in his throat. It was the start of a feverish taking and holding.

Without knowing quite how it happened, she found herself lying on the soft hearthrug, the wonderful weight of him pressing her down. The firelight was amber on her naked skin, and they were making love as fiercely as if they were appeasing an eternity of need.

She clung blindly to him and cried out, and then, as they reached the exquisite zenith of feeling together, an expression of clearness moved across her features and she lay quietly beneath him. For what seemed a pleasure-drugged forever neither of them moved.

Finally Ross shifted his weight, gathering her into his arms as though she was infinitely precious. She pressed her cheek against his hammering heart while her own pulse slowly steadied.

It was some moments before she stirred. As his hand gently stroked her back, she raised her head.

'You make me feel so beautiful,' she whispered. 'Do you realise we've never made love in front of the fire before?'

His fingers grazed the soft line of her cheek. A glint in his eyes, he said lazily, 'And I'd like nothing more than to do it again right now, but I think one of us should be ready to answer the door to our guests.'

Her hand flew to her mouth in horror.

'The dinner party! The doorbell could ring at any moment!'

She snatched up her clothes that were scattered on the Persian carpet and scrambled into them. Amusement tugged at the corners of Ross's mouth as, drawing on his shirt, he watched her agitated flurry. She swept her hair hurriedly away from her neck as she struggled to do up the zip of her dress.

'Here, let me,' he offered, laughter in his voice.

He fastened it for her, dropping a kiss on her nape as he finished. She turned round and saw that he was fully dressed, not a crease in the jacket that moulded his powerful shoulders. Flustered as she was, she was struck by his darkly handsome features, the aura of sensuality he possessed.

'Do I look all right?' she asked, her cheeks very flushed.

He drew her into his arms. 'Relax,' he teased. 'You

look gorgeous, and the evening's going to be a great success.'

The confidence in his voice quelled her flutter of nerves. She kissed him and flew into the dining-room to put the finishing touches to the table. Hardly had she had time to stand back and admire it before the bell rang. She left it to Ross to usher the first couple into the lounge.

When she joined them from the kitchen with a tray of cocktail snacks, he was pouring the drinks and already the atmosphere was convivial. Colin Mason had been Ross's best man at their wedding and Genieve liked both him and his wife, Maggie, a slender brunette with a warm personality. The four of them were chatting easily when the doorbell heralded the arrival of more friends.

The first half-hour flew by. Amid the lively buzz of conversation and laughter Genieve glanced across the room at Ross. The smile they exchanged was as intimate as a caress. Now that the misunderstanding between them was cleared up, she found she was no longer troubled by the prospect of having to entertain her spiteful cousin.

Coralie and Geoff arrived some twenty minutes late. She came into the lounge ahead of him, slim and smiling and scattering charm as Genieve, playing the part of the dutiful hostess, made the introductions.

In a silky turquoise dress with a deep neckline, her chestnut hair in an elegant twist, she looked stunning and, as ever, she radiated sex appeal. From her manner no one would have known that she and Genieve weren't still the best of friends.

Yet, for all her artificial bonhomie, there was a glint

of anger in her green eyes as over dinner her gaze shifted several times from Ross to Genieve and then back to Ross again. Piqued by the rapport between them, she trilled, 'Genieve, you must let me have the recipe for this chocolate mousse. It's simply mouthwatering!'

Genieve suspected her cousin knew she hadn't made it herself, but Ross intervened with humour, saving her from making the admission, 'Surely you know good cooks never divulge their recipes?'

The others laughed, and Maggie put in, 'It's certainly going to be a difficult act to follow!'

Genieve smiled, pleased that the meal had been appreciated, and thinking she must tell Faith and thank her again for her help. She was in the kitchen making coffee when her cousin came in and offered to lend a hand.

'I can manage, thank you,' Genieve said coolly as she set out the cups.

Coralie perched elegantly on a stool.

'I see I'm still out of favour for what I said the other day,' she commented mockingly.

'Very much out of favour,' said Genieve, her eyes sparking. She had trusted her cousin and she could not readily forgive her treachery. 'In fact, I didn't expect you to come this evening.'

'Why?' The lift of a self-willed eyebrow accompanied the question. 'You asked me to come, didn't you, and I assumed my husband was included in the invitation?'

'Your husband! You don't live with him, you'd cheat on him. . .'

'My word, didn't it get to you what I told you about Ross and me?' Coralie laughed.

'Yes, that was your intention, wasn't it?' Genieve said quietly. 'You hoped with your lies you could get me to leave Ross. And just in case that didn't work, you gave Paul my address hoping to cause more trouble. I expect it was you who told him I'd married Ross on the rebound!'

Coralie got to her feet, the taunting look on her face replaced by anger as Genieve confronted her with the truth.

'You should have married Paul!' she hissed. 'Ross belonged to me.'

'No, he didn't, but you'd have liked him to. That was why you tried to warn me off with that sweet little show of cousinly concern when you told me he wasn't my type. Then, when you saw us at the nightclub together, you were so furious you tipped your drink all over me. And the irony of it all is that even *then* I didn't see what you were playing at. I didn't see it because I looked on you as a friend!'

'Can women ever be friends when they're competing for the same man?' her cousin said derisively. Her green eyes cold, she went on, 'If you'd valued my friendship you'd have stayed well clear of Ross!'

Her cousin was a guest in her house, but, driven to striking back, Genieve retorted, 'I suggest you concentrate on sorting things out with your own husband instead of coveting mine! Geoff wants you to get back together, and presumably you haven't dismissed the idea entirely or you wouldn't be here with him this evening.'

'God, but you're naïve!' Coralie exclaimed, amused contempt in her laugh. 'You still believe in fairytale romance, don't you? The only reason I asked Geoff to come with me tonight is because there's a sale of Art Deco paintings coming up at Sotheby's shortly. I've set my heart on a couple of them and, if I play my cards right, Geoff might very well buy them for me.'

'You really are despicable!'

'I call it practical.'

'I feel sorry for Geoff,' Genieve said, meaning it.

'Feel sorry for yourself, little cousin,' Coralie snapped in reply. 'Your marriage is on shakier ground than you think.'

'You're jealous, Jealous that I'm happy with Ross.'

'Jealous!' her cousin scoffed. She snapped her fingers. 'I could take him away from you like that! And if you don't believe me, just watch!'

A man's voice enquired, 'Watch what?'

Coralie pivoted sharply and had the grace to blush as she saw her husband standing in the doorway, hands in his pockets as he lounged negligently against the frame. There was a sardonic light in his eyes. Recovering quickly, she gave him a cool smile, and said, 'You have such a gift for butting in when you're not wanted, darling.'

'You should run a charm school,' he returned laconically, unscathed by her sarcasm.

Coralie glared at him and, as his mouth quirked mockingly, she swept out of the room.

'Am I right in thinking my wife's been giving you a rough time?' Geoff asked Genieve.

She hesitated. She could hardly repeat what her cousin had been saying and, disconcerted by his question, she dropped her gaze. Geoff put a hand on her shoulder.

'Hey,' he said kindly, 'take no notice of her. She gets a kick out of being a cat at times.'

'I wish. . .'

'You wish what?'

She smiled ruefully.

'That certain things were different. You know, you're too good for her, Geoff.'

'No. I spoiled her. When we were first married I let her get away with murder.' His mouth twisted. 'It must be a weakness in my character.'

Genieve switched off the percolator, which had stopped bubbling and hissing.

'So what now?' she asked.

'God knows.' He shrugged. 'Shall I carry some of the cups through for you?'

'Thanks, that's nice of you.'

When she followed him into the lounge Coralie was talking to Ross. She was sitting on the sofa, smoking, her long legs crossed and tilted towards him, the angle of her wrist elegant and provocative.

Genieve handed the coffee round, too sure of her relationship with Ross to feel uneasy or jealous. A log shifted in the grate sending up a shower of sparks, and as it did so he caught her eye, the lazy glint in his gaze deliberately reminding her of their passionate lovemaking in front of the fire. She coloured prettily for a moment before resuming her conversation with the couple she was chatting to.

Maggie was the first to say, 'I'm afraid we must be going. It's even later than I realised.'

The other guests lingered for a while and then they, too, decided reluctantly that it was time to leave. Ross put his arm around Genieve as they stood at the front door and she waved goodbye as the last car drove away.

They went back into the lounge, where Genieve kicked off her shoes, enjoying the feel of the carpet under her stockinged feet. She sat down on the sofa, realising that, thanks to Coralie, the evening had been something of a strain.

'I think I'm going to rest on my laurels for a while after that,' she said jokingly.

Ross smiled and poured her a drink.

'I noticed you abstained while our visitors were here, so enjoy a nightcap now,' he said. 'You deserve it.'

'I'm glad it went off so well,' she commented, accepting the liqueur glass he handed her.

Pulling his tie undone, he joined her on the sofa. He put his arm round her, fitting the curves of her body to his as he drew her close.

'You were terrific,' he said, 'the perfect hostess, especially the way you handled Coralie. She may be your cousin, but if I were Geoff I'd be sorely tempted to put her across my knee and spank her. It might keep her in line.'

'I hope you've no intention of keeping me in line that way!' said Genieve, glancing up at him through her lashes.

He smiled wickedly. 'You know the saying, "a dog, a woman and a walnut tree, the more you beat them the better they be".'

'Chauvinist!' she said, thumping him playfully on the chest.

'Aren't I?' he laughed, grazing her temple with his lips.

She closed her eyes and laid her head against his

shoulder, lulled by the lateness of the hour and savouring the iron feel of him. She was almost dozing off when he took her empty glass from her.

Patting a yawn, she said, 'I'd better carry the glasses into the kitchen and see everything's tidy.'

'Leave it,' he answered. 'I'll see to it. You go to bed, you're tired.'

Too sleepy to argue, she did as he said. She left the bedside lamp on for him as she slipped between the covers. But though she was comfortable and drowsy she didn't drift off completely until he joined her.

She whispered his name, her body relaxing against the warm strength of his. His hand stroked the slim plane of her back and, kissing him absently, she fell asleep on a soft contented sigh.

CHAPTER NINE

HER skin golden in the early light, Genieve slid naked from the bed. Reaching for her wrap, she drew it on and went over to the window. Her silken hair was loose around her shoulders and she gathered it in her fingers at the nape of her neck, her body graceful, her raised arms emphasising the line of her breasts.

Ross watched her appreciatively, his hands clasped behind his dark head. His eyes stayed on her as she drew back the curtains and stood for a moment looking out with the pale autumn sunlight streaming into the room around her.

She felt profoundly happy, and her body seemed to glow with a sense of well-being. Conscious of her husband's gaze, she turned and smiled at him.

His chest and shoulders were broad and muscular, and the whiteness of the sheets and pillows emphasised his attractive swarthiness. Stretched out at ease in the rumpled bed, he was arrestingly male, virility stamped into every indolent line of him. Her heart contracted with love. Ross meant so much to her.

Smiling back, he said, 'Do you have any idea how lovely and desirable you look with the sun shining on your hair, and your wrap diaphanous against the light?'

It was crazy, when they had been making ardent uninhibited love only a short while before, that the word diaphanous should make her blush. But the glint in his dark eyes made her tantalisingly aware of her nakedness beneath her wrap.

'Come here.'

Obeying his command, she went and sat on the bed. Her fingers traced the strong line of his jaw as he pulled her to his chest. Mischievously she began, 'And you look. . .' She hesitated, searching for the word she wanted.

'Satisfied.' He found it for her, his deep voice lazy and caressing. 'But not so satisfied that I couldn't enjoy you all over again.'

Their gazes locked, the awareness so powerful between them that her blood began to tingle. Ross parted her wrap, easing it aside to reveal her breasts. A familiar hot melting pleasure went through her. He kissed her nipple and she caught her breath, her senses threatening to whirl her into total surrender again.

As he pushed her back against the pillows she protested huskily, 'I have to get up and get breakfast. I told Sherry I'd be at the boutique this morning to open up.'

'We could always skip breakfast,' he murmured, his lips finding the sensitive hollow at the base of her throat. 'My appetite this morning seems to be for other things.'

'Ross, don't,' she whispered achingly. 'I'll be late.'

Her fingers tightened on his strong shoulders as he stroked the incurve of her waist and she tried to fight the shivers of desire that quivered over her skin.

'You should have thought of that before you came back to bed,' he answered, but she knew from his voice he was teasing and intended letting her go.

He brushed her lips with his and she threaded her

fingers into his hair as they exchanged a long, intimate, pleasure-drugging kiss. Then, reluctantly, she slithered away from him, making her escape before his knowing hands could persuade her to stay in bed and consummate their love a second time that morning.

She was making a pot of tea when Ross joined her in the kitchen. He had showered and shaved and was dressed in a charcoal-grey business suit. She knew that he planned to work from home until midday, and envied his razor-sharp mind that enabled him to achieve in a morning what others would take the day to complete.

They chatted about various things as they had breakfast. Genieve found herself studying his face, the aggressive thrust of his jaw, the vertical grooves in his lean cheeks that deepened when he smiled. It was so different sharing the first meal of the day together now that the rift between them was repaired and they were sleeping together once more.

She finished her second cup of tea and said, rising from her chair, 'I must dash. I'll see you this evening.'

She expected to shrug on her jacket, pick up her house keys and leave the house without more ado, but to her surprise her keys weren't on the hall table where she usually left them. She moved the bowl of chrysanthemums, wondering if they had somehow got pushed behind it, then began to hunt through her bag for them.

'What have you lost?' asked Ross as he strolled into the hall.

'My house keys,' she said, feeling in her jacket pockets. 'I can't think what I've done with them. I know I had them on Saturday when I came in from the shop.'

'Take mine. I've got a spare set, and yours will turn up. I'll ask Faith to keep an eye open for them.'

'Thanks.'

She reached up on tiptoe to graze his cheek with her lips but, not satisfied with a fleeting embrace, he pulled her into his arms. His aftershave was crisp and bracing, a heady fragrance because it was so quintessentially male. He explored her mouth thoroughly before raising his head.

'Have a good day,' he said, his caressing voice sending a thrill down her spine.

'You too,' she murmured huskily.

She emerged from his arms slightly overwhelmed, a pleasureable and not unfamiliar sensation. She seemed to have been created for sexual homecoming with him, formed and fashioned to be his woman, his wife. What an absurd little sceptic she had been to doubt what they had, she chided herself as she left the house, to think, even for a moment, that it was her cousin Ross loved.

Feeling carefree and very secure, she drove to work. Though some of the trees were starting to look bare, the rowans and Norwegian maples were still bright in the sunshine. It was a blustery morning and the leaves were coming down like golden confetti. A sharp frost and autumn's waning splendour would give way to the grey bleakness of winter.

Genieve always enjoyed the wane of the year, but this morning she seemed even more aware of the beauty in the resting landscape with its palette of russet hues. It was wonderful knowing that Ross cherished her, that she was as important to him as he was everything to her.

She arrived at the boutique, where she began to

change the window for the start of the new week. Trade was always particularly good in the run-up to Christmas, with lingerie a popular choice of present.

She decided on a selection of exquisitely shaped, bias-cut nightgowns in silks and satins for the main window. Her assistant arrived as she was hanging glittering silver baubles in among the display. The opening of the door brought a current of chill air sweeping in.

'Isn't it cold this morning?' Sherry shivered, adding, 'The window looks lovely. Those baubles make it like an Aladdin's cave.'

Genieve smiled. 'I know it seems a bit early to be putting the decorations up, but I noticed as I came in that most of the shops are starting to look Christmassy. Last year we waited till after Guy Fawkes.'

'That's right, we did,' her assistant agreed, remembering. 'We had those very glamorous scarlet camisoles and slips in the window.'

'Yes, they sold well.'

'Didn't you give your cousin a matching set?' Sherry asked chattily as she went through into the workroom at the back of the boutique to hang up her coat.

'Yes,' said Genieve, a wry twist to her sensitive mouth. Coralie's spiteful double-dealing still hurt a little. Things would never be the same between them again. Moving the conversation on, she stated, 'I haven't given a thought to my Christmas shopping yet this year. I'm going to wait till the management course is over and then I'll be able to get my mind on it.'

'That won't leave you long,' warned Sherry, coming out of the workroom. 'Only six weeks.'

'Six weeks is heaps of time,' Genieve laughed. 'Some

people do all their Christmas shopping on Christmas Eve.'

'Well, I'm not one of them,' Sherry smiled. 'I like to have all my shopping finished early.'

Genieve was right to anticipate that business would be brisk over the next couple of weeks. She would have preferred, because of that, to have attended the four-day residential course at a slacker time, but there hadn't been a vacancy. The management college, which was set in a hundred-acre estate just outside Reading, had an excellent reputation, and its courses were always heavily subscribed.

She had known she would find the course useful. What she hadn't expected was that it would be so enjoyable. Excellently delivered, the programme was challenging, thought-provoking and stimulating. The emphasis was put on a practical approach, and particularly useful were the feedback sessions held during the evenings, which often went on until well after ten o'clock.

It was almost midnight and she was sitting up in bed, her brows drawn together in concentration as she pondered over a business problem, when the phone rang. Tossing the case study aside, she picked up the receiver.

'Ross!' she exclaimed with a little laugh of pleasure as she heard his voice. 'I didn't think you'd ring so late.'

'They're certainly working you hard. I gave you a call half an hour ago but got no answer.'

'The session finished officially at half past ten,' she told him, 'but, as none of the groups had come up with an answer to the case study we'd been looking at, we adjourned to the bar to carry on working on it.'

'Did you come up with a solution in the end?' he asked.

'Not one we could agree on,' she said with a smile. 'I'm reading the case study again now.'

'It sounds a lonely way to pass the night.'

The sensual note in his voice quickened her pulse. Cradling the phone against her ear, she said softly, her voice a shade husky, 'It is. I miss you.'

'I miss you too.'

She found she was smiling as she put the receiver down. Her last thought as she drifted off to sleep that night was that they would soon be together again.

The course finished on Friday morning after break-fast. It was raining steadily, and the heavily laden lorries that thundered along the motorway in the inside lane doused her windscreen with spray as she passed them.

She planned to stop off home before driving to the boutique to lend her assistant a hand. She had made good time on the journey and she wondered if she might just catch Ross before he left for work.

But his car wasn't in the drive, and the house was quiet as she let herself in. Telling herself it was silly to feel disappointed when she would see him that evening, she took her weekend case upstairs.

She walked into the master bedroom—then halted in the doorway, frozen with shock and horror. Her cousin lay asleep in the double bed which still bore the imprint of where Ross had lain beside her. She was utterly naked.

The case fell from Genieve's numbed hand. So many

emotions were surging through her that the room seemed to swirl dizzily. But above all, in that first sickening instant of shock, there was a mounting agony of pain.

Woken by the thud of the suitcase, Coralie stirred. She murmured Ross's name drowsily before turning over and opening her eyes.

'Genieve!' she gasped, reaching for the sheet and pulling it up to cover herself.

White with the frightful knife-thrust of her husband's betrayal, Genieve said, her voice low and trembling, 'You bitch!'

'I. . . I never thought you'd be back so early.'

'Obviously!' Fury rose up inside her, a tornado of rage and anguish. Picking up the first items of her cousin's clothing that came to hand, she threw them at her. 'Get dressed and get out of here! I could kill you for this!'

Coralie slithered out of bed, keeping the sheet wrapped round her.

'There's no need to fling my clothes at me,' she snapped.

'Count yourself lucky I don't fling you into the street this minute like the tramp you are!' Genieve hissed, her eyes burning.

She pivoted and swept out of the room, trembling with anger. She went downstairs and into the lounge. Her heart was pounding and she clutched at the mantelpiece to steady herself, the pain that squeezed her heart worse than any physical agony.

She clamped her throat shut to stifle the sobs that shook her shoulders. She would not give way to tears, she would not! Her cousin's triumph was great enough without letting her see that she was being torn apart by the proof of her husband's infidelity.

She lifted her head and turned as Coralie came into the room.

'I should have thought you'd have gone straight out of the front door.' She tried to sound cold and in charge of herself, but she could feel she was shaking with the force of her anger and despair.

Her cousin hunched her slender shoulders. 'There are some things that need to be said,' she stated.

'I don't wish to hear them!'

Ignoring her, Coralie said, 'I warned you that you wouldn't keep Ross happy for five minutes. You refused to listen. Well, now maybe you believe me.'

'You were determined this would happen!' Genieve accused, her eyes blazing in her white face.

Her cousin laughed spitefully.

'Yes, I was. You shouldn't have come between us. Except, of course, you haven't.'

Flinching inwardly, Genieve swung away. With her back to her cousin and her hands tightly clenched, she whispered furiously, 'Get out of here!'

She closed her eyes for an instant, fighting for self-mastery. Her poise, such as it was, would splinter in a tempest of wild and bitter tears if she had to endure another word.

But Coralie was enjoying her moment of vengeance. Coming to stand beside her, she taunted, 'How does it feel to know that I'm the one your husband loves, that your infatuation merely amuses him, that even in bed you fail to satisfy him? He told me so himself last night. Not that he needed to. I knew from the starving way we'd made love how much he'd missed me.'

'Get out!' Genieve hissed. 'Get out of here now, this minute! I never want to set eyes on you again. As far as I'm concerned, after today you don't exist!'

'But I certainly exist as far as Ross is concerned. Your marriage, darling, is over.'

The parting shot delivered, Coralie walked arrogantly to the door. It wasn't until she had gone that Genieve began to weep. Her sobs were painful, desperate, as she sat on the sofa, her hands covering her face, her head bent to her knees.

It had never entered her mind to question what Ross had told her on the evening of the dinner party concerning his relationship with Coralie. Blindly, trustingly, she had accepted his word.

From out of memory her cousin spoke. 'I could take him away from you like that!' Coralie had known all along that what she and Ross shared was strong enough for it to be rekindled at the first opportunity. When she'd said she and Ross had been lovers she'd been telling the truth.

Raw with pain and fury, Genieve went upstairs and tore the rumpled sheets from the double bed. But nothing could ease the agony inside her, only more tears, which when they were spent left her feeling numbed and still.

As Coralie had said, her marriage was over, yet she was too dazed to think of a course of action. Besides, before she walked out on Ross, she wanted to confront him. It was shattering to discover that mingled with her rage and hurt was the desperate desire to have him give her some kind of explanation, some lie that would mean she could still go on living with him as his wife. That was the measure of how much she loved him.

Her weakness and her lack of pride made fury well up inside her anew. How could Ross have betrayed her so cruelly? Why had he taken her love and then ripped it to shreds? Why had he chased her, when all along it had been Coralie he wanted?

She dropped her head in her hands, then started as the phone began to ring. Automatically she picked up the receiver, her hand tightening on it as she wondered suddenly if it might be Ross.

'Hello?' she began tersely.

'Is that you, Genieve?'

The tension in her melted as she heard her assistant's voice. She had thought herself empty of tears but, without warning, and for no reason, her eyes began to smart again. She had to force her voice to come.

'Yes.'

'I was worried when you didn't come into the shop. You said you'd be in by ten at the latest. Is everything all right? You sound upset.'

'I'm fine,' she lied huskily. She was anything but fine. She felt as though she had been dealt a body blow from which she hadn't recovered, but getting a grip on her emotions she said, 'I got back from Reading at about nine. I. . . I've been longer at home than I meant. I'll be in shortly.'

It flashed into her thoughts that the business was the only thing she had left. Everything else, everything that mattered, was in ruins. And torture though it would be to make small talk with her customers when her heart was breaking, it would be a hundred times worse to stay alone in the house when every thought brought with it another stab of pain.

'OK, I'll see you later,' said Sherry. 'But don't rush. I only called because I wondered where you'd got to.'

Her assistant rang off and Genieve went into the bathroom to splash cold water on her eyes. She reapplied her make-up and gazed at her reflection. She was still very pale, but no one would have known to look at her that she felt as though she had been kicked repeatedly, and the resulting ache beneath her ribs was almost more than she could bear.

She drove to work, parked, and sat for a moment in the car, gathering her strength. Then she got out and crossed the street to the boutique. Sherry was at the till ringing up a purchase as she walked in and there were two other customers browsing along the rails.

Screening her heartache, Genieve greeted her assistant in her usual friendly fashion. She was glad that the shop was busy, glad to be kept occupied. Custom was good all morning, and it was after one o'clock when Sherry said, 'What shall I get from the delicatessen? Do you fancy chicken or ham sandwiches?'

She didn't think she could force down either, but, determined not to go to pieces, she answered, 'I'll have chicken, but I'll skip the cheesecake today.'

The same grim determination got her through the afternoon. She contacted her suppliers and spoke to her accountant about a query, while all the time she marvelled that she could carry on so normally when she felt so chilled and numb.

It was raining again when she left the boutique. The pavements gleamed in the glare of street lamps and headlights. Her anguish had hardened now into a tight fierce knot of anger. More than that, she had come to a decision.

Confronting Ross with what had happened was point-
less. She must have been out of her mind to think they
had anything left to talk about! He wanted her cousin.
Well, he could have her, because she was going to drive
home, pack her things, and leave.

To let herself into the house and walk into her
bedroom to fetch her belongings was to realise that
inside she was an unexploded bomb of anger and pain.
The housekeepr had tidied the room while she had
been out and the bed was now made. Her weekend
case had been unpacked and put away.

Genieve felt her temperature rise as she stared at the
smooth cinnamon coverlet. Had she not stopped off
home that morning, she wouldn't have learned of
Ross's betrayal. She would have slept with him tonight,
let him make love to her in the very same bed where he
had enjoyed her cousin!

In a blaze of cold rage she crossed over to the
wardrobe. Her suitcase was open on the bed and she
was flinging her things into it when she heard Ross's
Jaguar draw up outside. Her mouth tightened and her
heart began to beat unevenly. She had hoped to be
gone before he came home.

She did not glance up from what she was doing, yet
she knew the moment he came into the bedroom.
There was an instant's silence as he observed her. Then
he demanded in perplexity, 'What exactly is going on
here?'

'What does it look like?' Her voice was cold and
expressionless. 'I'm packing.'

'I can see that,' he retorted, his clipped tone showing
irritation. 'What I want to know is why.'

She turned then. His black hair was slightly unruly in

a sensual sort of way from the rain. His expensive suit emphasised his masculine aura of success and virile power. She had thought she had her temper tightly in check, but at the sight of him, a tempest of hurt rose up inside her.

'You want to know why! Well, I want to know why, too!' she hissed with all the vehemence of pain. 'I want to know how you could do this to me.'

'Do what?' he snapped. She didn't answer and, pushed to the limit of his tolerance, he snatched hold of her wrist. 'Stop flinging things into that case and tell me what this is about!'

He forced her to face him and, acting instinctively, she raised her free hand and slapped him with all the force she could muster.

'Don't you touch me!'

The marks of her fingers showed red across one lean cheek and for a chilling instant she thought he was going to mete out retribution in kind. She backed away from the stunned look of anger on his face, the glittering fury in his dark eyes. The bed barred her further retreat and she gave a tiny cry of fright as he caught hold of her by the shoulders.

He pushed her so that she sat down abruptly beside her suitcase.

'My God, this has gone far enough!' he said in a voice that bit. 'You'd better start explaining yourself, Genieve, because my patience is exhausted!'

She would have scrambled to her feet, but he remained towering over her like a wolf ready to pounce.

'Oh, you're good,' she said resentfully. 'You're very good, coming the righteous husband when you've been cheating on me. When you and Coralie are lovers!'

Ross's dark brows came together in a scowl.

'How many times do I have to tell you there's nothing between me and your cousin?' he said savagely. 'Now what the hell's stirred this up again?'

'I'll tell you what's stirred it up! I came home this morning to find you'd spent the night with her!'

'Are you out of your mind?' He didn't spare the cold derision in his tone.

Genieve was on her feet, her eyes blazing, anger so fierce in her she was trembling with its force.

'You miserable liar! Wake up to the fact. I *know*! Coralie was here in our bed, naked, when I came home this morning!' Something flickered across the rugged planes of his swarthy face and she rushed on bitterly, 'Surprised I found out? I bet you are! You both thought I was so naïve!'

His glittering gaze pinned her. A nerve jumped in his tightly clenched jaw.

'Did you decide while you were away that you wanted to end our marriage?'

His stinging tone prompted her to flash, 'End it? It's over already. That's why I'm leaving. I'm going back to my place.'

As she spoke she slammed her suitcase shut and picked up her clutch bag.

'You're not walking out on me,' he rasped.

'You try and stop me! I'd sleep in the gutter before I'd spend another night here!'

His mouth thinned into a harsh line. Angrily he snatched her bag out of her hand.

'Give me that!' she demanded, but it was too late.

Ross was already tipping the contents of her bag out

on the bed. Snatching up her car keys, he said, his curt tone revealing the tight hold he had over his temper,

'You're not driving anywhere tonight till you've calmed down and I've got some answers out of you.'

'You can't keep me a prisoner here,' she said, her heart racing in panic.

'Can't I?' he ground back.

'If you won't give me the keys to my car,' she stormed, breathing rapidly, 'I'll take my case and I'll walk all the way to Harrow if I have to!'

His eyes were icy as they read the defiance in hers.

'Is that where you've arranged to meet Paul?' he jeered. 'I take it he's the one who's put you up to this.'

His accusation was so monstrously unfair that it stunned her for an instant. Then she burst out, 'How dare you? How *dare* you drag Paul into this when it's because of your infidelity that our marriage is over?'

Dark eyes slashed her with contempt. 'Still sticking to your story?'

'You bastard!' she breathed.

Going to the phone, she picked up the receiver. It was a bluff. She had no intention of getting involved wth Paul. She couldn't even remember his new phone number, but Ross fell for her desperate ploy.

'Who are you calling?' he demanded curtly.

'Paul,' she retorted. 'If you won't give me back my car keys I'm asking him to come and fetch me!'

Ross's nostrils flared and for a frightening moment she thought she'd gone too far. But his control was as great as the violence of emotion he was holding in check.

'You can save him the trouble,' he said harshly. 'And

you needn't bother to come crawling back to me when he dumps you a second time.'

Tossing her keys on to the bed, he strode out of the room.

CHAPTER TEN

GENIEVE was still trembling as she pulled on to the main road. Ross had made no further attempt to stop her from walking out, had not even come into the hall when she had descended the stairs.

She had driven off in the pouring rain and she had not glanced back. A tear traced down her cheek as she thought of how Ross had carried her over the threshold as his bride. To have given the house a farewell glance would have been to feel an agony of heartbreak greater than she could stand.

It was more than that she had been happy there. Ross was a part of herself. As his wife she had been complete. Now she was being torn assunder.

But although she had not glanced back, there was no stopping the playback of memory. How could Ross have appeared so loving on so many occasions and not have meant any of it? Why the pretence, when all the time it had been Coralie he wanted, Coralie he loved? Nothing made any sense any more, she thought wretchedly.

The street-lamps formed haloes in the steady downpour and the roads gleamed in their golden glow. With little traffic about, she was soon in sight of the Hill. She pulled up outside her cottage and let herself in. Tiredly she kicked the front door to behind her and set down her suitcase.

She glanced about the sitting-room, conscious of a

sudden rush of affection for the little house. It was like a haven, a bolthole where she could be alone and lick her wounds. She tried to dull the ache beneath her ribs by telling herself that eventually the pain would ease, but deep down she knew she would never get over Ross's betrayal. It would be with her forever.

She caught sight of herself in the oval mirror above the fireplace. She looked like a waif. Her flaming hair, darkened by the rain, fell in disarray about her shoulders. She was very pale and there were bluish shadows beneath her eyes. She thought of her slim, sexy and self-assured cousin, and realised that she hadn't stood a chance against such competition.

Hurt and fury welled up in her anew. Ross had come into her life like a hurricane force, wrecked her calm, and destroyed her independence. He had set out to win her and then, once she belonged to him, he had rejected her love and deceived her.

Why, why had he told her he loved her when it wasn't true? He had shown not one trace of guilt when she had told him she knew he'd spent the night with her cousin. Instead he had accused her of using it as an excuse to walk out.

Had he ever meant to be faithful to her? she wondered. Perhaps he hadn't. Perhaps she'd been naïve in thinking that marriage meant fidelity to him. Maybe he'd intended all along continuing his affair with Coralie.

Shattered by his lies, she got through the next few days in a state akin to someone recently bereaved. She couldn't eat and her nights were long and wakeful. Even when she slept out of sheer exhaustion it was a shallow, fitful sleep, with Ross her first thought on waking just as he was always her last thought as she drifted off.

It was Tuesday evening, and she sat on her bed, unpinning her hair which she had twisted into a topknot before having her bath. The cottage seemed very quiet, and her throat started to ache as she found herself remembering all the good moments in her marriage. She would never understand how her relationship with Ross could have seemed so strong when in reality it had been so shaky.

There was a knock at the front door and, roused from her thoughts, she glanced up. Hesitant about answering it when it was fairly late and she was wearing only a bathrobe, she went to the window and drew the curtain aside an inch to see who the caller was.

Her heart jolted at the sight of the tall man who stood outside with the light from the porch gleaming on his dark hair. Ross! Hurriedly she let the curtain fall back in place, her breathing quickened with agitation.

It was humiliating to discover that despite all her hurt and anger she yearned to see him; she had to see him. She went downstairs and opened the door, her lips parting as, to her surprise and dismay, she found she had made a mistake. It wasn't Ross she had glimpsed from her upstairs window, but Paul. Her disappointment was so acute that for a moment she couldn't find her voice.

'Hi,' he began, his mouth twisting with a mixture of wryness and resignation as he noted her reaction to his unexpected appearance on her doorstep. 'May I come in?'

'No. . . I. . . I'm not dressed.'

It was a pretext. She didn't want to ask him in and he knew it.

'Look, I understand how you feel,' he said, 'but it's important that we talk. Please, Genieve. I promise I won't stay long.'

It was chilly standing with the front door open and she was starting to shiver. Besides, she guessed from the quiet urgency in his voice that he wasn't going to take no for an answer. She hesitated and he repeated, 'Please! I'll go the moment I've said what I came here to say.'

Giving in, Genieve took a step back.

'All right,' she said tiredly. 'As long as you keep your word.'

'I suppose I couldn't expect to be very welcome,' he observed. 'I've caused you a lot of trouble, haven't I?'

She wasn't sure what he meant by that and she didn't enquire. Weary and heartsick, she didn't want to get into an argument that would prolong his visit. Paul sat down, keeping his overcoat on. She remained standing as she said, puzzled as the thought occurred to her, 'How did you know you'd find me here?'

'Coralie came to see me at my studio. She said. . .' He paused, then stated quietly, 'She said your marriage was running into problems and she thought you intended walking out on Ross.'

'What else did she say?' asked Genieve with a lift of her chin. The animosity she felt towards her cousin apparent from her tone, she guessed, 'That now was your chance to try to win me back?'

'Yes, she did say that,' he confirmed, his gaze intent on her face. 'She also said you'd never loved Ross, you'd only married him to spite me and that he meant nothing to you.'

The truth was so very different that pain swamped her. Ross had meant everything to her! He still did. She felt her lower lip begin to tremble. Paul murmured drily as she fumbled in the pocket of her robe for a handkerchief, 'Yes, well, not being totally bombastic and remembering how you fought me off when I tried to kiss you, I figured she'd got that part wrong.'

Genieve swallowed hard. Knowing that the only way to keep her tears in check was to change the subject, she said, as she sat down on the sofa, 'You still haven't said how you knew where to find me.'

'I wanted to see you, so I gave you a call at home. I don't know who I spoke to—your housekeeper, I think. She told me you weren't living there any more. I guessed you'd be here.'

'You guessed right,' Genieve answered, twisting her handkerchief in her hands.

'Why have you walked out on Ross?'

'I. . . I'd rather not talk about it,' she said in a cramped voice.

'Was it because of me?'

She couldn't believe he still harboured the illusion that there was life left in the embers of their affair. She had made it so plain that it was Ross she loved. Her nerves stretched to breaking point, she exclaimed in angry despair, 'For heaven's sake! Haven't I. . .'

'I didn't mean it like that,' Paul cut in. 'What I meant was. . .' Running a harassed hand through his hair, he tried to explain calmly to her. 'It. . .it was wrong of me to call round at your house that day. And it was doubly wrong of me to say what I did. I can imagine what your husband thought when he walked in, and the row it must have caused afterwards.'

Her silence verified what he had guessed and he went on, 'You were upset that day. You wouldn't tell me why, but I think it was because there was already friction in your marriage. What I want to know is, was it Ross walking in and finding the two of us together that finished everything? Because if it was I'm prepared to go to him to tell him what really happened.'

Genieve's gaze went to his. He truly cared about her, she realised numbly, for all the cavalier way he had treated her in the past.

'Do you want me to corroborate your version of things?' he prompted. 'Would it help?'

'It. . .we didn't break up over that,' she whispered.

'Then why did you break up?'

'Over something else altogether,' she said huskily, adding, a tight knot of emotion in her throat, 'But I. . . I'm really grateful to you for coming here and. . .'

Her voice caught and he said wryly, 'I hoped for once to do something unselfish where you were concerned. Look, isn't there any chance that you and Ross. . .'

'No,' she broke in throatily. 'It's over. I. . . I'll always love Ross, but I can't live with him any more.'

There was a short silence and then Paul drew a deep breath and got to his feet.

'Well, I said I wouldn't stay,' he stated. 'Take care of yourself, Genieve.'

She knew he was saying goodbye to her and that she wouldn't see him again. As he opened the front door she faltered, genuinely and deeply touched by the concern he had shown for her, 'Paul. . .'

He paused on the threshold and she joined him there.

'Thanks,' she said with husky eloquence.

Grateful to him, she reached up and kissed him goodbye on the cheek. His arm went round her, holding her tightly before he strode off down the road to where his car was parked under a nearby street-lamp.

Genieve closed the door behind him, glad that they had parted as friends and yet, at the same time, very close to tears because talking about Ross had brought all the misery rushing back. He had scarcely been gone more than a few minutes when the bell rang. Thinking he must have forgotten something, and so called straight back, she opened the door again.

Her heart lurched, not only with shock but in response to the vibrantly male figure standing in front of her. The navy jacket he was wearing, over jeans and a pullover, the collar slightly turned up, made Ross's eyes look almost black, while its cut emphasised the broad power of his shoulders.

They stood staring at each other, Genieve too startled to say anything initially, while Ross appeared to be too angry. She noted the clenched set of his jaw, the flare of his nostrils. Her temper suddenly catching fire from his, she snapped heatedly, 'I don't know why you've come, but I have *nothing* to say to you!'

She made to slam the door shut, but Ross promptly thrust his foot inside the jamb. The door went swinging back on its hinges and, with no option except to retreat, she fell back.

She continued to retreat until the distance of the room separated them. She had never seen Ross look so savage, or so dangerous, and her mouth was dry.

'Get your things,' he ground out between clenched teeth. 'I'm taking you home.'

'No!' She was as fierce as a cornered animal. 'I'm not coming!'

'I said, get your things!' he ordered, advancing threateningly towards her.

'I won't!' she flashed defiantly, then gave a tiny cry of fright as he grabbed hold of her.

A muscle twitched along his lean jaw, the tightness of his rugged features indicating the immense effort with which he was controlling his fury.

'You may not want to leave this little love nest,' he rasped, 'but you're my *wife*, damn it! And you're coming home with me!'

'This isn't a love nest,' she denied. 'I don't know what you're. . .'

'You lying little bitch!' he cut across her. 'Not two minutes ago you were kissing your lover a passionate goodnight. I saw you as I pulled up across the street.'

'It wasn't. . .'

In no mood to listen to her protests, he snarled, 'Did Paul take you in front of the fire while he was here, the way you and I made love that time? Did he, or did you make use of the bedroom?'

'Paul's not my lover!' she spat at him, too angry herself now to be frightened by the force of his fury. Pierced by hot rage and hurt, she blazed, 'How dare you accuse me of giving myself to him?'

Ross's dark eyes narrowed on her. His gaze seemed to burn her, but she would not drop her own that was molten with defiance.

'Then what was he doing here?' he sneered. 'Or do you entertain all your visitors in a bathrobe?'

'I don't have to explain myself to you!'

'That's where you're wrong. No woman makes a fool out of me!'

'That's all you care about, your damned pride!' Genieve cried, anguish strangling her voice as she wrenched herself free, 'Well, let me tell you something. I wish I had slept with Paul. I wish I'd cheated on you, the same way you cheated on me. Only even if I had still been attracted to Paul, I still couldn't have done it. And you know why? I couldn't have done it because I *meant* my marriage vows!'

'If your marriage vows were so sacred then why did you walk out on me?'

'You know full well why I walked out on you. How would *you* have felt if you'd come home to find me in bed with Paul? You're even jealous of the friendly goodbye kiss I gave him. But I was supposed to take your infidelity, your cheating, your deception in my stride!' She snatched up her glass that was on the coffee-table. 'I didn't even offer Paul a drink while he was here. The only glass here is mine, the one. . .'

She broke off with a startled cry of pain, the glass falling from her hand as she stared in horror at the welling line of bright blood that ran across her palm. In her fury and despair she had snapped the narrow stem of the liqueur glass in two.

His face tight with concern, Ross was beside her in a second.

'You little fool, what have you done?' he muttered, taking hold of her hand.

Numbly she noticed the masculine line of his mouth thin as he saw the long deep cut. He shrugged off his jacket. Then he was escorting her upstairs and into the bathroom, his hands authoritative yet gentle as he pushed her on to the bathroom stool. Dizzy and shaken, she offered no resistance.

Her palm smarted unbearably as he bathed the cut, but worse by far was the ache in her heart as she silently submitted to his ministerings. Her eyes went to his chiselled features as he dried her fingers, pressing the soft towel carefully on either side of the cut.

Against her will she remembered the gentleness in his hands on other occasions. She recalled their love-making, the sensual mastery of his touch as he expressed his delight in her. Had he caressed Coralie with the same erotic passion and tenderness? The jealous thought made her catch her breath.

Ross glanced at her. His black brows drawn together in a frown, he asked, 'Did I hurt you?'

'Yes!' she choked fiercely, then averted her head as she realised he was referring to her hand. 'No. . .' she amended huskily. 'I. . .it doesn't matter. I. . . I was thinking of something else.'

'Something more painful even than your cut hand?' he questioned, and then, when she refused to answer, he said, his tone sardonic, 'There's just no fathoming you, is there? In what way did I ever hurt you?'

'As if you didn't know!' she flashed, adding coldly, 'The first aid kit's in the medicine cabinet. If you'll pass it to me I can manage.'

'Stop being so bloody independent!'

Genieve was more shocked than she had realised from cutting her hand, and his harsh tone made her nerves break abruptly. Without warning two tears brimmed her eyes. As her vision blurred something flickered across his face, a suggestion of exasperation with himself, almost of pain.

A forced note of calm in his voice, he said, 'I'm sorry, Genieve. I didn't mean to snap at you.'

'Really?' she said coldly.

She saw his jaw tighten and was glad that her reply had angered him. Anything was better than his impersonal compassion.

He put some antiseptic on the cut, then said evenly as he finished bandaging her hand, 'I'll get you a drink and then you and I are going to talk.'

Back in the sitting-room he picked up the broken glass and then poured her a brandy. She sat on the sofa without looking at him, trying to master her emotions. She knew from the quiet stillness she sensed in him that this was only a lull before the next confrontation.

She accepted the brandy he handed her in silence, colouring slightly as his gaze swept over her, lingering an instant on the shadowy valley between her breasts. She was suddenly as aware as he evidently was that beneath her bathrobe she was naked. Tension of a different sort began to vibrate the air.

'I think you should go,' she said in a tight voice.

Her hand went to the lapels of her robe, drawing them together, and his mouth quirked cynically as he observed the defensive gesture.

'Relax, Genieve,' he said sarcastically. 'Desirable though you are, and much as I miss you in bed, I didn't come here tonight to rape you.'

'I want you to go,' she repeated.

'And I want some answers,' he fired back.

'To what? What good is it going to do to go over it all again?' she asked, bitterness and pain flooding back as she went on, 'You weren't faithful to me for five minutes. There's nothing you can say that will make me consider coming back to you and giving our marriage another try!'

His hawkish dark eyes, that were as sharp and keen as his mind, held her fixed. He stood, tall and powerful, a ruthless male interrogator there was no appeasing.

'Tell me,' he said coldly, 'when did the two of you first hit on this particular story?'

Her chin lifted, her puzzled gaze meeting the glitter of contempt in his.

'What story?'

'Don't act naïve with me!' he rasped. 'Was it you or was it Paul who came up with the idea of claiming that I was involved with your cousin?'

'Claiming you were involved!' Genieve said with a bitter laugh.

She saw his mouth tighten and her pulse quickened with the static that crackled between them. Coupled with the dangerous sexual awareness was a fierce smouldering enmity.

'Did you cook up the accusation that I was having an affair with your cousin so you'd have grounds for a divorce and could marry Paul? Was that the motivation?' he rapped out.

'Do you think I don't know what I saw?' she hissed. 'How long are you going to pretend you didn't make love to Coralie that night? Why don't you admit that it was always her, not me, that she was the one you wanted to marry, that you took me as second best?' She was on her feet. 'Why, in God's name, don't you admit the truth?'

His jaw clenched with anger at her outburst. Snatching his jacket up from where he had flung it over the back of a chair, he advanced towards her.

'Yes, that's right,' he said harshly. 'I had your cousin in bed with me every night you were away.'

Genieve flinched. She had known it was the truth, but to hear him say it was to feel almost sick with pain. Ross took hold of her chin, compelling her to look at him none too gently.

'I not only slept with Coralie, but she was damned good!' he said brutally. 'That was what you wanted to hear. Well, now you know!'

Releasing her, he strode out of the cottage, slamming the front door behind him. There was a roar of acceleration as his car sped away and then a silence, broken a few minutes later by the soft, despairing sound of her crying.

CHAPTER ELEVEN

DEVASTATED by the break-up of her marriage, Genieve was glad she had the boutique to go to every day. Without it the anguish would have driven her almost crazy. The fact that Christmas was fast approaching seemed to emphasise her loneliness. She felt bereft. Yet that wasn't her only torment. Worse was the stab of jealousy as she wondered how long it had taken, after she had told Ross she was never going back to him, before he called Coralie.

In an attempt to push the misery to the back of her mind she steeled herself to concentrate on her plans for the new boutique. She didn't think she would ever be fully able to come to terms with the fact that her marriage was over, but she had to try to let go of her shattered dreams and look to the future. The business had meant a lot to her in the past. Perhaps, some day, when the sense of angry futility that enveloped her lifted a little, it would mean as much again. She had to believe that.

Since Sherry occasionally needed to contact her at home she had been forced to tell her that she had left Ross. Her assistant had been both surprised and perplexed, but she had accepted her short explanation that things hadn't worked out. Genieve was grateful that, while she'd commiserated, she hadn't pried or probed in any way.

The subject wasn't referred to again by either of

them until Genieve came into the boutique one morning and announced that she had upped her offer on the
new premises and it had been accepted. As she hung
up her coat in the workroom she said, 'We'll be able to
open the second shop as soon as the alterations are
completed.'

'But I thought. . .' Sherry began as she came to stand
in the doorway. 'I mean. . .don't you need to keep
your cottage? How are you going to raise the capital?'

'I've already sold my cottage,' Genieve told her. 'We
exchange contracts in a fortnight's time.'

'Where are you going to live?'

'In the flat over the new shop. It's a bit cramped, but
it will be handy to be on the premises,' Genieve said,
adding questioningly, 'I thought you'd be pleased.'

'I am,' Sherry replied, then laughed, 'I'm delighted!
It's just that when you said you and Ross had split up,
I assumed everything was off, that you'd need your
cottage to live in. I'd given up all hope of managing the
boutique.'

'For a minute you had me worried!' smiled Genieve.
'I was afraid you were going to tell me you'd changed
your mind.'

'No way! I'm only sorry. . .' Sherry broke off, and
said awkwardly, 'Well, you know.'

Genieve did know. Sherry was happy for herself, but
sorry for *her*. She found that a little hard to bear
because she was trying so hard to pretend she hadn't
been completely ripped to pieces by walking out on
Ross. Evidently her act wasn't as good as she had
thought.

So far she hadn't felt able to tell her parents that her
marriage was over. As she wandered through the

crowded department stores on Oxford Street one Saturday doing her Christmas shopping, she supposed she would have to break the news to her family soon.

She looked at the displays of merchandise, the leatherwear, sweaters, gloves, the sports equipment, and, foolish as it was, she found herself wanting to buy something for Ross. The sentimental desire was swiftly followed by an upsurge of angry bitterness. Ross had never loved her. The reason why he had chased her remained a mystery. All she knew was that she hated him for making her love him. And she only had to remember how he had thrown the admission at her that he had slept with Coralie to find she was trembling with fury.

Although it was December, it was still mild for the time of year. But the trees with their winter shapes gave a bleakness to the landscape, and on days when it was misty or wet, evening set in early, and it was dark by half-past three.

It was on such an evening that Genieve was alone in the boutique. The shop had been fairly quiet all afternoon and Sherry, who had a dental appointment, had already left. Not expecting to get another customer when it was so near to closing time, Genieve began to tidy the counter.

The shop bell tinkled as the door was opened briskly and Ross walked in, his black hair gleaming from the rain. Genieve looked up, finding that her heart was suddenly hammering.

Tall and vitally male, the power of Ross's charisma seemed for an instant to throw her totally off balance. She couldn't drag her gaze away from his darkly handsome features, so fierce was the pain and pleasure she felt on seeing him. Her eyes began to smoulder with the force of the emotions surging through her.

'What do you want?' she began coldly. 'You can't do that!' she protested as he flipped the sign on the door to Closed.

He cocked a dark eyebrow at her.

'You're hardly likely to get any customers when it's pouring with rain outside and only ten minutes to closing time.'

His slightly sarcastic tone stirred up her simmering temper. Coming round from behind the counter, she snapped, 'You don't know that.'

She made to turn the sign back, but Ross's hand shot out, encircling her wrist.

'Let go of me!' she demanded, antagonised by the live warmth of his grasp.

'Do you want me to wait till it's dead on half-past five and we'll talk then?' he asked sardonically.

He had bested her, as he invariably did in any argument. She let out an angry sigh of defeat, and he released her.

'What do you want?' she asked, her tone inimical.

His gaze narrowed on her, hawlike and perceptive. Ignoring her question, he observed, 'You look thinner.'

'I'm not pining away, if that's what you're thinking,' lied Genieve. 'I've been kept very busy seeing about the new shop. If I've lost weight it's because of that.'

'I hoped you might have missed me.'

Certain he was mocking her, she pivoted sharply, her poise beginning to splinter. Keeping her back to him, she scoffed, 'Did you?'

She tensed as he took hold of her by the arm, compelling her to face him.

'Yes,' he said with quiet ferocity, his chiselled features set in hard lines. 'If I hadn't I wouldn't have bothered to come round with these.'

Taking her hand, he dropped a set of keys into them. She looked down at them, then raised her gaze to his, failing to see their significance.

'Why should I want my house keys?' she asked.

'You recognise them?'

His dry inflexion made her snap,

'Of course I do. They're the ones I lost.'

'You're not curious to know where I found them?'

'Not particularly, no,' she said. 'What is this? Why are we playing Twenty Questions with my house keys?'

'Because you *didn't* lose them,' he answered. 'Coralie pocketed them the evening she came to our dinner party. That's how she let herself in that Friday morning after I'd left for work, that's how she was naked in our bed when you arrived home from your course.'

'I. . . I don't believe you,' she said, doubt in her voice, and then anger as the recollection came back, 'You admitted you slept with her!'

'I was being sarcastic. Surely you knew that!'

'No, I didn't!' she retorted, glaring at him.

His jaw tightened as their eyes clashed. But remaining calm, though it clearly cost him some effort, he said, 'You wouldn't let go of the accusation that I'd slept with your cousin. I thought it was a deliberate fabrication so you could leave me for Paul. In the end I lost my temper.'

This time Genieve didn't answer. Her fingers tightening in suspense on the keys she held in her hand, she waited for him to go on.

'I didn't start to fathom Coralie's little game until I

tracked Paul down at his studio last week. I intended warning him to stay away from you in the future. He not only agreed, he told me why he'd visited your cottage that evening.'

'I suppose he also said I'm in love with you.' Genieve tried to make her voice sceptical as she cut in.

She didn't want him to know that it was true. It would give him such power to manipulate her.

'Stop interrupting and listen,' he ordered, his brows lowering in a frown. 'When I finally worked out what must have happened I went to see your cousin. It took me quite some time to get her to confess, but in the end she told me the truth. That's why you couldn't find your keys. Coralie had them. She set you up. She set us both up.'

'She couldn't have,' said Genieve. 'She didn't know about the management course. She didn't know that I'd be away, or that I'd come home that morning. . .'

'Think about it,' Ross cut across her, the tightness in his cheek muscles showing how important it was to him that he convince her. 'The topic came up over dinner. That was when Coralie must have got the idea. To lift your house keys from the hall table was child's play after that.'

Genieve bit her lip. Her mind was whirling with thoughts. She so desperately wanted to believe him and she was so terribly afraid of being hurt again.

'For God's sake, woman!' Ross exclaimed. 'Do I have to drag you along to your cousin's so you can hear her admit it yourself? Think about what I'm saying. It fits.'

'Perhaps that's the trouble,' she retorted, her heart beating unevenly because she was so close to being convinced. 'It fits too well. How can I be sure you're not making this up?'

He swore suddenly, his anger coming to the fore when still she doubted him.

'There's just no convincing you, is there?' he rasped. 'You can't even trust me when you've got the evidence in front of you. When that artist you got entangled with cheated on you, he destroyed your ability ever to put your faith in anyone again!'

'That's not——'

'No?' he cut in angrily before she could finish. 'When I first met you and you put up such barriers against me, I understood because I knew you'd been hurt. When you accused me of loving Coralie, of wanting to marry her, not you, I sought to reassure you. I didn't realise then, there just is no reassuring you. Well, you know something,' he swept on, 'I've had it. I've had it up to here. I've had waiting for you to show you have some kind of faith in me. I thought I could repair the damage Paul had done, but I was wrong. You want to cling to your blinkered beliefs? OK, you go ahead!'

He strode to the door and, numbed by his enraged and frustrated outburst, she took an instant to find her voice and say, 'Ross. . .'

She was too late. The door slammed shut, the bell jangling furiously. Her fingers shook slightly as she opened her palm and stared at her keys. It had all been too much to comprehend at once, but now it was falling into place.

She remembered how Coralie had flounced out of the kitchen the evening of the dinner party when Geoff had walked in. It would have been the perfect opportunity for her to take the keys, especially after claiming that she could take Ross away from her.

She remembered Coralie sitting up in bed and clutching the sheet to her with a horrified gasp. She'd been too distraught at the time to be objective, but now, looking back, she could see how theatrical it had been. Coralie's surprise, her dismay, had all been an act. No wonder, Genieve thought, that Ross had been so baffled and so angered by her accusation.

For an instant she felt almost dizzy with reaction. It was as if she had been snatched out of a yawning black pit and the brightness was dazzling. Ross loved her! She felt her eyes begin to sting, she was swamped with such a giddy sense of relief.

She knew she must rush after him, apologise for her lack of trust. Ross had made it very clear that she had tried his patience and understanding to the limit. She had to go to him, beg him to forgive her, tell him she'd make it up to him. She refused to heed the tiny cold niggle of apprehension that perhaps he wouldn't want to listen. She was too happy and relieved.

She hurried into the workroom and tugged on her scarf and coat. In her haste she dropped her gloves. She snatched them up off the floor, reached across her desk and was ready to switch off the light and lock up when the phone started ringing.

She looked at it and paused. The temptation to ignore its ringing was enormous, but the call might be important and she'd be away from the shop until Monday. Quickly she picked up the receiver.

It was the estate agent.

'I hoped I'd catch you before you left this evening,' he began. 'The buyers of your cottage are having some difficulty over the mortgage as the property is over two hundred years old. I'm afraid there's bound to be a hold-up while this is sorted out, and I know you need the money for your transaction to go ahead.'

'Is it all right if I get back to you about it?' asked Genieve, not wanting to be delayed. 'I'm sorry, but I'm in a hurry.'

'I don't want to hold you up. But could I just clear up a couple of points while you're on the line?'

Inwardly she sighed. Unable to bring the call to a speedy end, it was some ten minutes later before she left the shop.

Impatient to get home, she ran in the teeming rain to where her car was parked, and pulled away. But her hopes of making good time on the drive were dashed the moment she turned on to the main road. Her heart sank as she joined the long tailback of cars that crawled along behind a giant mechanical digger that was travelling at a snail's pace.

As she inched along, the niggle of worry in her mind which she had ignored at first began to grow. What if she had pushed Ross too far with her refusal to believe him? She was ready to concede that he had a right to be angry. Even after he had explained she had clung stubbornly to her suspicions, but as he had said himself, her cousin had set her up. Not only that, but she'd done a first-class job of it. Surely Ross couldn't blame her for finding it hard for a moment to credit the truth?

Eventually she managed to overtake the mechanical digger, but even after that the drive was slow, with a lot of traffic on the roads. By the time she drew up outside the house she was so afraid that perhaps she had wrecked everything with her scepticism, her mouth felt dry and her heart was beating unevenly.

The curtains were drawn at the lounge window and a

chink of light escaped. Genieve shut the car door behind her. Although it was still raining hard she hesitated for an instant, needing to summon up her courage. Then she ran for the shelter of the porch and let herself in.

Ross was sitting in an armchair near the fire as she walked into the lounge, his legs stretched out in front of him. He had shed his tie and jacket, and his white shirt emphasised his attractive swarthiness.

A bottle of whisky was on the coffee table and his long fingers were curled around the glass he was nursing. Her pulse quickened at the sight of him. He looked arrestingly male, cynical and very hard to placate.

'I was just planning to get good and drunk over you,' he said sardonically, slanting her a brooding glance. 'To what do I owe the honour of your presence? Did you forget something?'

Genieve ran her tongue over her parched lips.

'I know you're angry. . .'

'Sharp of you to notice,' he cut in. 'Do you want to go upstairs and check the bedroom to make sure your cousin isn't in there?'

Her nerves were stretched tight, and his mockery made her quick to flare, 'Don't you turn your sarcasm on me! I came here to say I'm sorry.'

Ross's dark eyes held her fixed in the silence that followed her statement. He got to his feet, the nerve that twitched in his jaw indicating that if she was trembling inwardly as the racking moment dragged on, he, too, was tense. He set his glass down on the mantelpiece.

'That could mean several things,' he said at last. His

tone faintly derisive, he asked evenly, 'What exactly are you sorry about?'

'Not. . .not trusting you,' she said in a whisper. She swallowed. 'Ross, I. . . I've thought about what you said, and it. . .it makes sense. I know you weren't unfaithful to me and I'm sorry I accused you the way I did. But if. . .if you can't forgive me for continuing to doubt you I. . . I'll understand and I'll go.'

Her voice trailed off. In an agony of suspense she waited for him to answer, her heart jolting with hope as she saw the harsh lines of his face soften. As once before when she had stood before him, hurt, vulnerable, unsure and desperately needing his love, he said with husky tenderness, 'Come here.'

She didn't need to be told twice. She flew across the room, to be enveloped in his embrace. He held her so tightly she could scarcely breathe, but she didn't care. She was so choked with happiness that she didn't want him ever to let her go.

The words were unnecessary, but she said them anyway.

'Do you forgive me?'

'Of course I forgive you.' He released her a little to gaze down at her face and then, as though he were afraid she might vanish, he hugged her close again. 'Sweetheart, don't ever walk out on me again,' he said raggedly.

'I won't,' she whispered. Her fingers caressed his strong back. 'I never meant to be so unreasonable. When you came into the shop and told me what had happened it was all too much to grasp.'

'You had me at my wits' end,' he told her, sitting

down in the armchair and pulling her on to his knee in one smooth movement.

He helped her out of her coat and she said, 'I wanted to believe you, but I. . . I was frightened to. I was afraid it might not be true and then there'd be all the hell of losing you again.'

'You could never lose my love. It was yours from the first moment I saw you.'

She linked her arms around his neck, everything that was in her heart mirrored in her smoky-blue eyes.

'Oh, Ross, I've been so miserable without you!'

As she nestled closer to him he bent his head, his mouth finding hers in a kiss of deep tender urgency and passion. Her lips parted willingly, joy coursing through her. Ross kissed her long and thoroughly, and when at last his lips left hers there was a hot glow in her eyes and an answering hungry desire in his.

Shivers of pleasure danced over her skin as his hand that had slid beneath her thick burnished hair stroked her neck. The whole evening lay ahead of them and to savour each kiss, each endearment, each caress could only heighten the pleasure of their lovemaking now that everything was settled between them.

'How did you work it out?' she asked softly. 'How did you know Coralie had stolen my house keys?'

'I first started to tumble to it after I'd called round at your cottage that evening. The trouble was, my jealousy of Paul kept getting in the way. After I'd been to see him I started thinking more clearly. You were so hurt and so fierce, my love, I realised that, fantastic as it seemed, you must actually have seen Coralie in our bed. I tried to work out how you could have done, and then I remembered your lost house keys. And I remembered, too, that they'd disappeared immediately after the dinner party.'

'Coralie must have watched you drive away that Friday morning and then let herself in,' Genieve said, still marvelling at the way her cousin had planned it all. 'She was so convincing, the act she put on. She even taunted me, saying you found me disappointing in bed.'

Ross chuckled. Throwing one of the cushions on to the floor, he pulled her down with him on the carpet in front of the fire. 'You surely didn't believe that!' he said, finding her mouth again.

'I didn't know what to believe,' she admitted with a smile, after they had exchanged a long, tantalising kiss. Genieve traced the masculine line of his mouth with her fingers and then brushed her lips against his. 'Until all this happened I actually harboured the sentimental notion that one day Coralie and Geoff would get back together again.'

Ross smoothed a stray tendril of hair away from her face.

'I wouldn't discount it,' he said. 'Geoff still loves her. When you love for better, for worse, for richer, for poorer, you don't give up. Not ever.'

Her heart contracted as she gazed into his eyes. That was the way Ross loved her, she realised. Even if she hadn't come to him tonight, even if she had gone on doubting, he still wouldn't have let her go.

And then her thoughts swirled, her mind closed to everything save the sensation of him as his lips, warm and authoritative, claimed hers, while his knowing fingers unfastened the buttons of her blouse. The kiss they exchanged was long, deep and needful.

Outside a gust of wind blew the rain against the window pane. It was a raw December evening, but inside, with the firelight flickering, all the magic, wild sweet passion and warmth of love was theirs.

Next month's romances

Each month, you can choose from a world of variety in romance with Mills & Boon. These are the new titles to look out for next month.

THE STEFANOS MARRIAGE Helen Bianchin

THE LAND OF MAYBE Sandra Field

THE THREAT OF LOVE Charlotte Lamb

NO REPRIEVE Susan Napier

SOMETHING FROM THE HEART Amanda Browning

MISSISSIPPI MISS Emma Goldrick

RANCHER'S BRIDE Jeanne Allan

A VINTAGE AFFAIR Elizabeth Barnes

JUNGLE LOVER Sally Heywood

ENDLESS SUMMER Angela Wells

INHERIT YOUR LOVE Sally Cook

WILD CHAMPAGNE Kate Kingston

PORTRAIT OF A STRANGER Helena Dawson

NOT HIS PROPERTY Edwina Shore

Available from Boots, Martins, John Menzies, W.H. Smith, Woolworths and other paperback stockists.

Also available from Reader Service, P.O. Box 236, Thornton Road, Croydon, Surrey CR9 3RU.

Readers in South Africa — write to:
Independent Book Services Pty, Postbag X3010, Randburg, 2125, S. Africa.

An irresistible offer from Mills & Boon

Here's a personal invitation from Mills & Boon Reader Service, to become a regular reader of romance. To welcome you, we'd like you to have four books, a CUDDLY TEDDY and a special MYSTERY GIFT absolutely FREE.

Then each month you could look forward to receiving 6 more Brand New Romances, delivered to your door, post and packing free! Plus our Free newsletter featuring author news, competitions and special offers.

This invitation comes with no strings attached. You can cancel or suspend your subscription at any time, and still keep your free books and gifts.

Its so easy. Send no money now. Simply fill in the coupon below and post it to - **Mills & Boon Reader Service, FREEPOST, PO Box 236, Croydon, Surrey CR9 9EL**

--- NO STAMP REQUIRED ---

Free Books Coupon

YES! Please rush me my 4 Free Romances and 2 Free Gifts! Please also reserve me a Reader Service Subscription. If I decide to subscribe I can look forward to receiving 6 brand new Romances each month for just £8.70 delivered direct to my door, post and packing is free. If I choose not to subscribe I shall write to you within 10 days - I can keep the books and gifts whatever I decide. I can cancel or suspend my subscription at any time. I am over 18.

Name Mrs/Miss/Ms/Mr _____ EP87R

Address _____

_____ Postcode _____

Signature _____

mps
MAILING
PREFERENCE
SERVICE